HIGH ELVES

BY ADAM TROKE

CONTENTS

By: Adam Troke.

Original Book: Rick Priestley. **Additional Material:** Bill King. **Cover Art:** Paul Dainton. **Illustration:** Paul Dainton, Nuala Kinrade, Neil Hodgson, Karl Kopinski, John Blanche, Geoff Taylor & Dave Gallagher. **Graphic Design:** Pete Borlace & Alun Davies. **Miniatures Sculptors:** Aly Morrison, Trish Morrison, Martin Footitt, Gary Morley, Mark Harrison, Alex Hedström, Dave Thomas & Colin Grayson. **'Eavy Metal:** Fil Dunn, Pete Foley, Neil Green, Neil Langdown, Darren Latham, Keith Robertson, Anja Wettergren & Kirsten Williams. **Hobby Material:** Dave Andrews, Neil Hodgson, Mark Jones, Chad Mierzwa & Dominic Murray. **Production:** Talima Fox, Marc Elliott, Sean Turtle, Tim Vincent, Mark Owen, John Michelbach, Stuart White & Ian Strickland. **Special Thanks To:** The Geeks play-testers, Brian Folcarelli, Marko Lukic, Roy Eggensperger, Mark Havener, Mike Marshall, Mat Ward, Graham Davey, Jeremy Vetock & Alan Merrett.

UK	US	Canada	Australia	Northern Europe
Games Workshop Ltd.,	Games Workshop Inc.,	Games Workshop,	Games Workshop,	Games Workshop Ltd.,
Willow Rd, Lenton,	6711 Baymeadow Drive,	2679 Bristol Circle,	23 Liverpool Street,	Willow Rd, Lenton,
Nottingham.	Glen Burnie,	Unit 3, Oakville,	Ingleburn	Nottingham.
NG7 2WS	Maryland 21060-6401	Ontario, L6H 6Z8	NSW 2565	NG7 2WS, UK

INTRODUCTION

Ulthuan is the island home of the High Elves. It is surrounded on all sides by the most sinister of enemies, and only through the skill of their armies have the High Elves survived some of history's most devastating wars. The High Elves are a race much reduced by conflict, but their armies are renowned across the world for their ruthless proficiency. This book is the definitive guide to collecting, painting and playing with a High Elf army in games of Warhammer.

The Warhammer Game
The Warhammer rule book contains the rules you need to fight battles with your Citadel miniatures. Every army has its own book that works with these rules and allows you to turn your collection of miniatures into a battle-ready force. This particular Army Book describes the High Elves of Ulthuan.

Why collect a High Elf Army?
The High Elves are the most skilled warriors in the known world. Every Elf in the force is blessed with dexterity and agility enough to strike a charging knight from his saddle before his lance can hit home. The mainstay of the High Elf army are the citizen warriors who form the Archer and Spear regiments, in turn these are bolstered by elite fighters such as the legendary Sword Masters and the proud Dragon Princes of Caledor.

The High Elf army allows you to create a force to suit your own tastes, from a host of knights and chariots that races towards the enemy, to one that valiantly holds its ground, destroying the foe with clouds of arrows and ranks of infantry. Whichever you choose, your army will be resplendent with shining armour, glittering spears and billowing standards!

How This Book Works
Every Army Book is split into five main sections that deal with different aspects of the army. Warhammer Armies: High Elves contains:

The Elves of Ulthuan. The first section introduces the High Elves and their deeds in the Warhammer world. It details the long and bloody history of the High Elves and the many grievous wars that have shaped the proud people of Ulthuan.

The Forces of Ulthuan. Every unit type and hero in the High Elf army is examined here. You will find a full description of each entry, alongside complete rules and details of any unique abilities they possess.

Collecting a High Elf Army. Here you will see photographs of the range of Citadel miniatures available for the High Elf army, gloriously painted by Games Workshop's renowned 'Eavy Metal team. Colour schemes for the different units in the High Elf army, example forces and a wealth of useful information can all be found in this section.

High Elf Army List. The army list takes all of the warriors presented in the previous section and arranges them so you can choose an army for your games. Units are classed as either Characters, Core, Special or Rare Units and can be taken in different quantities depending on the size of the game you are playing. Each model also has a points value to help ensure you can pit your army against an opponent's in a fair match.

Vaul's Forge. The final section of the book lists all the magical items that your High Elf models can be equipped with, including weapons, armour and other ancient and powerful items.

Find Out More
While Warhammer Armies: High Elves contains everything you need to play a game with your High Elf army, there are always more tactics to use, different battles to fight and painting ideas to try out. The monthly magazine White Dwarf contains articles about all aspects of the Warhammer game and hobby, and you can find articles specific to the High Elves on our web site:

www.games-workshop.com

THE HIGH ELVES

The origins of the High Elves are rooted in the nativity of the world, when they were birthed onto the island paradise of Ulthuan. Among the oldest and greatest of all the civilised races, the High Elves are graceful where lesser mortals are clumsy, noble where they are crude.

The High Elves were once the greatest and most powerful race in the whole world and their actions shaped history. Now the High Elves are a race in its twilight; long and bitter wars have ravaged their once great empire and the High Elf race has begun to dwindle. The beautiful cities of Ulthuan become quieter each year, no longer bustling with vibrancy and life but shells of their former glory. Facing this steady decline, the High Elves remain resolute and unbowed.

Children of Ulthuan

All Elves are fair to behold and of them all the High Elves are the most handsome. High Elves are pale-skinned with fine, aesthetically beautiful features and hair as fine as flax. High Elves are tall and proud in their bearing, indeed it is not uncommon for an Elf to stand a whole head taller than a man. They have a slim build, which has led to the common misconception that Elves are weak or fragile. In fact, the opposite is true, for Elves are surprisingly strong, and though they are not as robust as the races of Orcs or Dwarfs, they more than compensate for that with their dexterity and amazing agility.

Elves are long-lived, some say immortal, and less vulnerable to disease than humans. Every movement that an Elf makes is graceful and controlled, their minds are quick and clever with an intensity and depth of insight which makes them seem fey and strange to other races. High Elves convey meaning into the slightest gesture, perceiving a wealth of information in the slightest nod of a head, or narrowing of eyes. More than once the Lords of Ulthuan have made war amongst themselves or upon other races for some real or imagined slight, for though they are a noble people the High Elves can be cold and haughty, unreasoning in the view of other races.

Asuryan - The Creator God

Asuryan, the Emperor of the Heavens, is the oldest and greatest of the Elf gods. He is the Creator and the Flame Eternal, the giver of life, rests in his hand. The Elves believe that it is his purpose and plan that they follow.

Asuryan dwells alone in a great pyramid atop the Heavens, and observes the world from his diamond throne. Because no mortal has ever looked upon his countenance, all statues of him bear a mask.

Asuryan is the judge between the disputes of the gods. He rarely meddles in the affairs of mortals, but it is he who protects the Twin Thrones of Ulthuan.

The Art of War

For their diminishing race to survive, the High Elves must possess an army of unequalled skill to fend off their many enemies. To this end all High Elves are taught the arts of war from an early age and swiftly master the sword, spear and bow. This strict policy of service means that Ulthuan can boast armies far larger than her diminished population would suggest. These citizen soldiers form the core of Ulthuan's armies, expertly trained warriors, resplendent in white robes and shining armour. Those of noble birth are taught to bear the arms of the Silver Helms, the magnificent Elven knights who fight in the vanguard of the High Elf army. Cavalrymen almost without peer, they are renowned for crashing through enemy shield walls, their sharp lances striking down their foes. High Elf generals must take great care with the lives of their warriors though, for the population of Ulthuan diminishes each year, and every loss is hard to bear.

While all Elves make effective warriors, those who completely devote their lives to the martial arts can be measured among the most deadly fighters in the world. Other High Elves choose to make warfare their way of life for different reasons, driven to violence through despair and sorrow or in pursuit of wisdom. The Shadow Warriors of Nagarythe are grim soldiers who fight for revenge alone. By contrast, the White Lions of Chrace are noble and fair, and devoted solely to the protection of the Phoenix King of Ulthuan.

High Elves bring their finely honed aesthetic not only to martial prowess, but to the very arms and armour they use. All High Elf weaponry and accoutrements of war are meticulously and elegantly crafted. Swords are often passed down from father to son, and may be ancient family heirlooms that have drawn blood in thousands of battles. The armour worn by High Elves is beautifully fashioned from tiny metal scales making it lightweight and flexible, allowing the wearer to maintain their natural swiftness and agility. High Elves decorate their armour and weapons, making each a fantastic work of art. Their tall shapely helms glitter in the sunlight and are often intricately carved and encrusted in precious gems.

The High Elves have developed sorcery far beyond the accomplishments of any other race. They were the first to study magic and remain the greatest masters of it in the known world. Through magic the High Elves protect their island home of Ulthuan, for without the conjurations of the High Elf mages the entire island would sink beneath the waves forever. High Elf mages are mighty spell casters whose fiery blasts and awesome energies have won many a battle. It is the Elves who in years past taught magic to men, although the Elf mages far surpass the human wizards of the Old World in both skill and knowledge.

ULTHUAN

The High Elf civilisation was born on the immense island-continent of Ulthuan, an island paradise created specifically for the High Elves by the Old Ones who first shaped the world. Situated in the Great Western Ocean, between the Old and New Worlds, Ulthuan resembles a hollow ring of land, surrounded by scattered archipelagos. The ring is broken only at its southern point by the Straits of Lothern. These provide the only sea route between the island's Inner Sea and the ocean beyond.

Ulthuan itself is divided into the Outer and Inner Kingdoms. The former being those whose shores touch the ocean, while the latter are those that surround the Inner Sea. The Inner and Outer Kingdoms are divided by a range of titanic cloud-piercing mountains known as the Annulii. The Annulii are almost impossible to cross, save by certain passes and tunnels and these are guarded by massive fortified gates and watched over by companies of grim Elven warriors. So few are these passages between the Inner and Outer Kingdoms, that most communication between them takes place by sea, for the Elves are masters of the waves and the journey is often faster aboard a swift Elven ship.

Ulthuan is a place of incredible magic, where unthinkable power is harnessed and borne upon gentle winds. The raw power of the land is clear for all to see. From the multi-coloured skies high above the Annulii Mountains, that shift and swirl with roiling energy, to the lush and verdant inner lands that know no winter, the majesty and splendour of Ulthuan is undeniable.

A network of great menhirs, vast standing stones each engraved with potent magical runes, stretches across the continent of Ulthuan from shore to shore, channelling and calming the dread magics that are drawn towards Ulthuan. Each standing stone collects the raw power and directs it to its inward neighbour, ever closer to the Inner Sea and the centre of the magical vortex at the heart of Ulthuan.

In ancient days, in a time known as The Sundering, the continent was literally torn apart, riven by terrible magic that wracked the land and threatened to sink it beneath the waves. Only at the last moment was Ulthuan saved, and now, only the most powerful spells and wards keep Ulthuan afloat. Without the vast power drawn in by the menhirs, these protective wards would fail and the whole continent would be swallowed up by the sea.

Ulthuan is ruled by the Twin Thrones of the Phoenix King and the Everqueen, a tradition of leadership that has been unbroken for many thousands of years. Beneath the King and Queen are Ulthuan's noble families, who take up much of the burden of ruling the island continent. Rival noble houses strive constantly with one another for dominance within the courts of the Phoenix King and the Everqueen, eager to improve their personal standing, along with the status and perception of their realm.

In ancient days the Kingdom of Nagarythe was the most prestigious of all the Elven realms, but in later days, such glory has passed instead to the Inner Kingdoms, specifically Caledor and Saphery and most recently Eataine.

> ### The Vortex of Magic
> *The Annulii Mountains are riven with mystical energy, which drifts to Ulthuan on the unsteady Winds of Magic. Ulthuan itself acts as a focal point for the winds of magical power that blow across the known world from the Northern Wastes. These drifting energies are drawn to Ulthuan, like water in a whirlpool, forming a vortex of magic.*
>
> *In this way Ulthuan drains magic out of the known world and prevents the tide of magic overwhelming everything and turning it into a seething realm of Chaos.*
>
> *The creation of this magical vortex was one of the first and greatest acts of the High Elf mages of Ulthuan – keeping the entire world safe from destruction.*

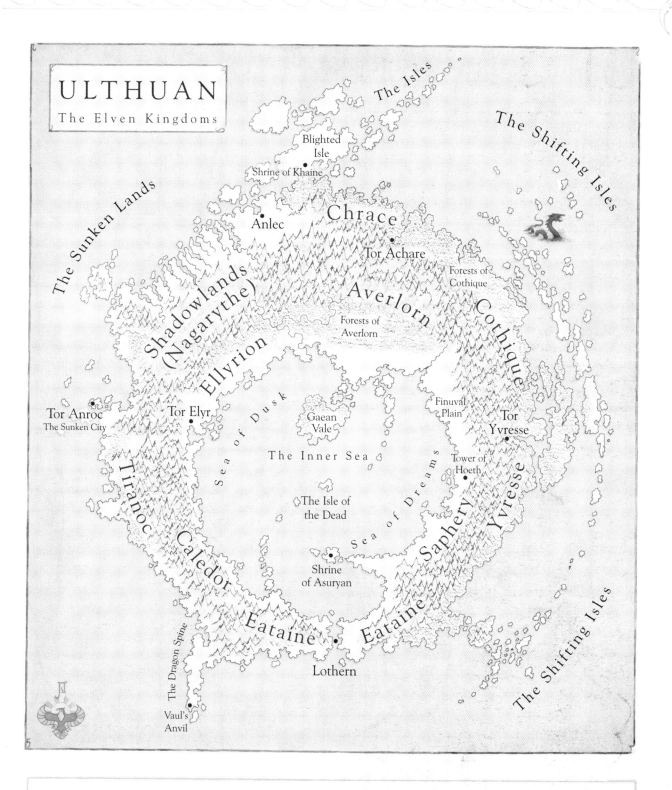

ULTHUAN
The Elven Kingdoms

The Isles

The Shifting Isles

Blighted Isle

Shrine of Khaine

The Sunken Lands

Anlec

Chrace

Tor Achare

Forests of Cothique

Shadowlands (Nagarythe)

Averlorn

Cothique

Forests of Averlorn

Ellyrion

The Sunken Lands

Tor Anroc
The Sunken City

Tor Elyr

Sea of Dusk

Gaean Vale

Finuval Plain

Tor Yvresse

The Inner Sea

Tower of Hoeth

The Isle of the Dead

Sea of Dreams

Tiranoc

Caledor

The Isle of the Dead

Saphery

Yvresse

Shrine of Asuryan

The Dragon Spine

Eataine

Eataine

The Shifting Isles

Lothern

Vaul's Anvil

T or Achare's foundations were laid in the years following the death of Aenarion and it has endured relatively unchanged since those halcyon days. Carvings of Aenarion's foremost generals stare proudly from alabaster cornices, capstones and finials, in death watching over a people their heroism preserved in life. Statues of Caledor the Great and Aenarion the Defender loom over courtyards, marble giants filigreed with gold and set with glittering gemstones. They tower over the masses just as their deeds eclipse those of their descendants. In modern times Tor Achare is a lynchpin of Ulthuan's defences both martial and mystical. Its garrison boasts nigh twenty thousand souls, waiting in readiness for the next inevitable battle. Archers and spearmen, knights and nobles all train within the walls, harnessing six thousand years of combat experience to serve the most disciplined army the world has ever known. Tor Achare is also a vital part of the Waystone network. Should it be destroyed, the disruption would unshackle vast tides of raw energy and so doom the entire world.

THE INNER KINGDOMS

The Inner Kingdoms, set within the twilit ring of the Annulii, are shielded from contact with the outer world by the mountains that surround them and the buffer states of the Outer Kingdoms. Many of the inhabitants of the inner lands are introverted and dreamy. They make scholars, mystics and sorcerers without peer, but all too often are affected by a languor that means they rarely bestir themselves except for the most pressing and dire of circumstances.

Eataine

As the realm from which the current Phoenix King comes, Eataine is considered first among the Elf Kingdoms. However, it is simply the hinterland of the vast city-state of Lothern. It is the most southerly of the kingdoms of Ulthuan, carved in two by the Straits of Lothern, the only inlet to the Inner Sea from the great ocean beyond. Eataine's lands are dotted with vineyards, villas and summer estates to which the noble families of the city retire. The city is the real centre of power and source of Eataine's prosperity. It is one of the wonders of the known world and no-one who has ever visited it can forget it.

Approaching Lothern, the first thing a mariner sees is the Glittering Tower, a great lighthouse filled with thousands of lamps, situated on a rocky isle in the mouth of the treacherous waters of the Straits of Lothern. This titanic fortress guards the approach to the Emerald Gate, the first sea-gate of Lothern. Anyone approaching the Emerald Gate can easily be caught in a crossfire between the great war engines in the Glittering Tower and those on the Gate itself. The sight of these great bastions is enough to turn all but the most insane attackers away.

Any who are allowed passage through the Emerald Gate pass through the wide channel of the Straits, sheer cliff faces lined with ramparts all constantly garrisoned by well-armed and alert warriors of the Sea Guard. A second portal bars the way for those who are not permitted access, a vast gate of shining silver set with sapphires the size of a man's head, beyond which lies a huge lagoon where thousands of vessels of every conceivable size and shape, from tiny pleasure craft to mighty warships of the High Elf fleet lie at anchor. Around this lagoon sits Lothern itself, and this is as far as any non-Elf may travel. Visitors are free to sample the delights of the city, to gaze in wonder at the two-hundred foot high statues of the Phoenix King, the Everqueen and the mighty Elven Gods, but they are forbidden to travel through the third gate of ruby and gold and into the Inner Seas.

Caledor

Caledor is a thinly populated, mountainous realm to the west of Eataine. In elder days several of the Phoenix Kings of Ulthuan came from here and the kingdom enjoyed a power far beyond its sparse population would suggest. The reason for this can be summed up in one word - dragons.

These mighty creatures made their lairs beneath the blazing peaks of the Dragon Spine Mountains. Nestled within these bleak volcanic highlands are fertile valleys filled with game plentiful enough to satisfy even the appetites of dragons. Here, long ago, Caledor Dragontamer bound the fearsome dragons to his will, using harnesses of enchanted truesteel smelted in the fiery heart of Vaul's Anvil. His descendants named their kingdom Caledor in his honour.

In battle none could stand against them, for the Dragon Princes of Caledor were fearsome warriors and their steeds were terrible to behold. Though the Dragon Princes were few, the destruction they could wreak was unmatched.

Eventually the volcanoes erupted less and the mountains cooled. As the peaks lost their fire so too did the dragons lose theirs. One by one they drifted into slumber, becoming ever more difficult to rouse. As the strength of the dragons waned so did the power of the Dragon Princes. The long reign of the Dragon Princes ended and their grip on the throne of the Phoenix King was lost. Soon other realms, including the fast-rising mercantile city-state of Lothern in Eataine, eclipsed the old realm of Caledor.

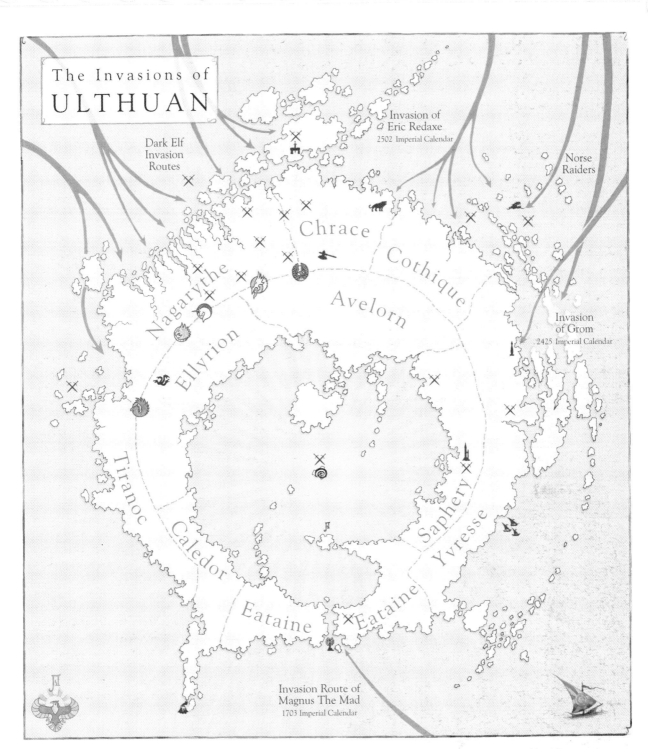

The Invasions of ULTHUAN

Dark Elf Invasion Routes

Invasion of Eric Redaxe
2502 Imperial Calendar

Norse Raiders

Chrace

Cothique

Avelorn

Nagarythe

Ellyrion

Invasion of Grom
2425 Imperial Calendar

Tiranoc

Caledor

Saphery

Yvresse

Eataine

Eataine

Invasion Route of
Magnus The Mad
1703 Imperial Calendar

Crucial Landmarks

 The Tower of Hoeth

Vaul's Anvil – Temple of Vaul

The Shrine of Asuryan

Altar of Khaine

The Isle of the Dead/The Vortex

The Glittering Tower Lighthouse

Sites of Interest

Watch stone of Athel
Tamarha – rebuilt after
the invasion of Grom

Albreth's Cove – home of
Sea Master Albreth's fleet

Leviathan-infested waters

Here Korhil slew Charandis

Site of the ambush where
Caledor I was saved by
Chracian woodsmen

Gauma, the 11-headed
Hydra is slain by
Laerial Sureblade

Battle site

Gates

 Eagle

Griffon

Unicorn

Dragon

Phoenix

Ellyrion

Ellyrion is a land of gentle summers and mild winters, where herds of Elven Steeds thunder across the sweeping plains. Touched by beneficial magics, and fed on the long grasses of the steppe, the steeds of Ellyrion are the swiftest and most noble of four-legged beasts. Fast as the wind and loyal unto death, they are the perfect mount for Elf nobility. They are also the envy of the Dark Elves, who go to great lengths to plunder Ellyrion steeds for use by their own cavalry.

Ellyrian Horsemasters maintain constant cavalry patrols across northern Ulthuan to warn of invasions by Dark Elf or Norse raiding fleets, and Ellyrian Reaver Knights are famed throughout Ulthuan for their hardiness and prowess in battle.

Tor Elyr is the single great city in the Kingdom of Ellyrion, and is found on the coast of the Sea of Dusk. It is built on a series of island castles linked by a web of silver bridges. Each castle is a palace, sculpted from the living rock of a peaked island. Tor Elyr's walls stand proud and defiant on the landscape, pennants fluttering on the wind. Ellyrion Reavers are expected to spend days on the march, sleeping in the saddle as need dictates, and it is to Tor Elyr that the dauntless cavalrymen of Ellyrion come to rest when they return from their long sweeps through the coastlands.

Avelorn

North-east of Ellyrion, across the river Arduil, lies the great Forest of Avelorn, most ancient of all the Elven realms. Upon its tangled groves ancient glamours lie, and under its eaves creatures of legend still walk. Treemen tend the wild gardens of oak and suntree. Great Eagles nest in the enchanted hills, and Unicorns walk in its sun-dappled glades. The Elves that live here are a strange, fey breed who share much in common with the Wood Elves of Athel Lothern.

Avelorn is ruled by the Everqueen, the chosen of the Earth Mother, mistress of the undying forest, preserver of green fastness, observer of the rites of the golden spring, occupant of one of the Twin Thrones of Ulthuan.

Summer lies eternally on Avelorn's enchanted glades. Beneath the leafy bowers the golden subjects of the Everqueen dance and sing. The court of the Everqueen moves through Avelorn from place to place like a great carnival, pitching silken pavilions of myriad colours wherever it halts. By day, silver laughter rings through the forest as the Elves make sport. By night, faery lights flicker in the darkness, drifting behind the Everqueen's courtiers and illuminating the revels and feasting. With its perfect weather, bountiful forests and beautiful near-immortal inhabitants, Avelorn seems the sort of rustic paradise of which mortal men can only dream.

Yet beneath this carefree surface bitter enmities stir. Factions at the Evercourt vie for the favour of the Queen. Old rivalries are barely submerged and every quip has a deadly double meaning. For prestige is treated as a matter of life and death in Avelorn. To be chosen as the Queen's handmaid is the highest honour for an Elf-maid or her family, just as to be chosen as her consort is the dream of every youth of Avelorn. All in the Everqueen's court seek to enhance their status at the cost of their rivals. The most trusted of the Everqueen's courtiers are the Maiden Guard - a regiment of one hundred Elf-maids schooled in the arts of war till they equal or exceed even the greatest Elven knights with spear and bow. At all times these beautiful warriors accompany the Everqueen, both her advisors and her protectors.

With so many journeying to Avelorn to join the court of the Everqueen, it is unsurprising that many of Ulthuan's greatest heroes can be found there. These competitive lords flock to Avelorn and there engage in contests, great feats of arms, horse riding and archery in an effort to prove their prowess to the court and perhaps catch the eye of the Everqueen herself.

Vaul's Anvil

Caledor is the location of Vaul's Anvil, the fiercest of all volcanoes. Upon this blazing black island at the very tail of the Dragon Spine sits the great shrine of Vaul, god of smiths. His temple rests in a great tower of black adamant rising out of the steaming lava within the volcano's crater. The temple can only be approached over a narrow drawbridge of truesteel. Within this shrine the blind priests of Vaul forge weapons of power and devices of infinite cunning for use by the Elf Lords.

Vaul is the Maker. He is both crippled and blind, wounded in the ancient wars of the gods when he challenged the might of Khaine the War God. He is forever chained to his anvil, enslaved to the will of Khaine, forced to make magic weapons of extraordinary power for the War God in a never-ending battle against the great enemy.

The priests of Vaul ritually blind themselves when they enter the Order of Vaul. The act of putting out their eyes has greater significance than merely leaving the priests sightless. While they lose their earthly vision, they gain something far more. They are bestowed with the skill and shrewdness of their patron deity, and the understanding of the sorrow and suffering that Vaul has undergone to protect the Elves. This knowledge and wisdom enables them to harness the Winds of Magic and thus create enchanted weapons of incredible potency for the High Elves who fight the wars to protect Ulthuan.

Saphery

South and east of Avelorn, on the shores of the Sea of Dreams, lies Saphery, the land of wizardry. The heart of Saphery is the Tower of Hoeth, the shrine of the God of Wisdom. This is the greatest repository of magical knowledge in the world, compiled down the centuries by High Elf mages and scholars, many of whom still dedicate their lives to the accumulation of magical lore. The Tower of Hoeth rises high above the forest. This bone-white structure is almost half a mile high, a feat of engineering made possible only by magic. It was built over twenty centuries ago on the orders of the Phoenix King of the time, Bel-Korhadris, the Scholar King. The tower stands at the point of a great confluence of the coursing magical energies of the vortex, a fact that lends it a greater strength than any creation of mere bricks and mortar.

From anywhere in the kingdom of Saphery, the Tower of Hoeth can be seen as a sharp white needle of stone thrusting into the sky. Its approaches are guarded by rings of illusion and mazes of spells which means only those permitted by the Loremasters of Hoeth ever find a true path to the tower. Those who seek wisdom and enlightenment at the shrine will find it. Those who seek power are never seen again.

The Tower of Hoeth is also the home of the Sword Masters, warrior-ascetics who dedicate their lives to the pursuit of wisdom and learning controlled violence. They study meditation and martial arts until they are capable of amazing feats of arms. The Sword Masters favour the greatsword, wielding it with more skill than an ordinary warrior could attain. The Sword Masters are the agents of the Loremasters of Hoeth and of the Phoenix King. The Supreme Loremaster will often dispatch them to deal with threats to the interest of the Tower and the Kingdom.

Beyond the spell-walls of the Tower of Hoeth are the domains of the nobles of Saphery. The Princes of this realm are mages of awesome power. They are reclusive and idiosyncratic, dwelling in exquisite mansions with only their families and a select band of retainers. Each noble's home has its own character reflecting the interests and magical researches of its patrons. The palace of Anurion the Green, for example, is surrounded by terraced gardens containing many strange and exotic plants, some carnivorous, some sentient, some obviously enchanted. Some of his collection are not even of this world.

The mages of Saphery and their personal guards are often summoned out of their seclusion by the Phoenix King to aid him in his wars. In times of war some of Saphery's mages have proven to be both great warriors and statesmen in their own right. Many of the mages from the land of wizardry can be found leading mighty armies in strange and out-of-the-way parts of the world.

THE OUTER KINGDOMS

Tiranoc

Tiranoc is the westernmost realm of Ulthuan. Once it was the fairest of the Elf lands. Majestic snow-capped peaks towered over sweeping flower-strewn plains. The people were great sailors who colonised much of the eastern New World. Wealth flowed from these colonies: gold to gild the city spires, silver to be wrought into the bodywork of their chariots, furs for winter wear and medicinal herbs to cure the sick. The charioteers of Tiranoc, famed throughout the land for their skill and daring, raced between their white marble cities. The folk were content and peaceful and their lives golden. But this time of happiness was to pass.

In the dark time of the Sundering when the Dark Elves broke with the people of Ulthuan, Tiranoc suffered grievously. At the climax of the war the Dark Elf mages unleashed such loathesome magics and the High Elf mages responded with such potent counter spells that the whole of Ulthuan was devastated. Tiranoc was flooded by the sea and disappeared almost completely, leaving only a fraction of the once great kingdom above the ocean, with their greatest cities ravaged and their mercantile districts beneath the seas.

Many of the survivors swore to rebuild their kingdom to its former glory. Over the millennia they have slowly done so, and there are once more prosperous cities in Tiranoc. The folk of that kingdom have not forgotten the past though, and in their hearts burns a bitter hatred of the Dark Elves.

The Shadowlands

This dark and desolate region was once part of a mighty Elven Kingdom called Nagarythe. During the reign of the first Phoenix King, Aenarion held court here with his Queen, the sinister Morathi. The Elves of Nagarythe fought against Chaos for many long years until Aenarion finally triumphed and the world was freed from the perils of the Dark Gods. That desperate struggle hardened and embittered the Nagarythe, so that other Elves came to regard them as a cruel and bloodthirsty people. After Aenarion's death, his son by Morathi, Malekith, inherited the kingdom of Nagarythe, which he ruled from his court in Anlec for many years until the time of the Sundering.

When Malekith rose against the rightful Phoenix King, he led his warriors in a savage and destructive war. Nagarythe was destroyed and many of its people fled with their evil master to the cold lands of the New World. They became the Dark Elves – evil kin to the High Elves of Ulthuan. Today what little remains of the once proud Kingdom of Nagarythe is treated with fear and distrust, and is known as the Shadowlands. It is uninhabited but for wanderers and beasts.

The mighty fortress of Anlec, from where both Aenarion and Malekith ruled the once proud people of Nagarythe, was destroyed during the Sundering. Since that time the Dark Elves have returned more than once to reclaim their ancient Kingdom, but each time they have been expelled by the High Elves. The ruins of Anlec have been refortified, fought over, and cast down again more than once, and even today they draw the Dark Elves back to the lands of their ancestors. Some whisper that more Elves have died fighting over Anlec's ruins than anywhere else in Ulthuan.

The Isles

The Isles of the North suffered most during the Wars of the Sundering. Here cataclysmic forces were unleashed that drowned the land and shattered the northern part of the continent. The remaining islands are tortured and twisted places, blasted by fire and death, and near lifeless. Such life that does survive is warped from contact with the pools and flows of dark magical energy left over from the war. Monsters, stirred from the lightless ocean depths by the sinking of the lands, sometimes come ashore here in search of prey.

This realm once belonged to the Elves of Naggaroth and they still seek to reclaim it. The Elves of Ulthuan maintain fortresses and watchtowers in these desolate lands to warn them against invaders. Year by year war is waged here. Sometimes the Isles are in possession of the Dark Elves, sometimes in possession of the warriors of the Phoenix King. This is truly a sundered land.

Rising over the misty wilderness of the Blighted Isle, largest of the surviving islands, is the great shrine of Khaine, the War God of the Elves. This shrine has long been abandoned but it is still a place of great power and of deep significance to both the High Elves and the Dark Elves. Both worship Khaine as a god and both claim his shrine.

The Shrine itself is a massive black altar within which is embedded a weapon of immeasurable power. Everyone who looks upon it sees a different weapon whether spear, sword or axe. All agree that the weapon drips blood, and those who have dared look upon it can feel it singing to their soul, filling them with promises of violence and destruction.

Chrace and Cothique

In the elder days the kingdoms of Chrace and Cothique were relatively empty lands, occupied only by those who sought to escape the more civilised realms and return to nature. Now they exist in a state of permanent war.

Chrace is the main route through which the Dark Elves seek access to the Inner Lands. Troops constantly move through en route to war with the Dark Elves. As the war has gone on, the lands have become perilous. The isolated communities of the wooded highlands have been fortified. The locals are great hunters and scouts, adept at guerrilla warfare and skilled with bow, sword and axe.

The hunters of Chrace maintain a constant watch on the passes through their lands, and they are swift to act if Dark Elf raiders are sighted. When the Dark Elves are spied Great Eagles are despatched to summon reinforcements while the Chracian regiments are mustered to hold back the enemy. The Archer and Spear regiments formed by the hardy Elves who live in the mountains are among the best in Ulthuan and they ambush and destroy any Dark Elves who dare to trespass in their realm.

The mountains of Chrace are the home of the fearsome white lions and to be counted as a real hunter, an Elf of Chrace must kill one of these mighty beasts single-handed. The white lion also gives its name to the legendary regiments in the service of the Phoenix Throne: the White Lions, carefully selected warriors who guard the Phoenix King.

Cothique is a coastal kingdom, inhabited by shrewd and hardy seafolk. Their graceful vessels plough the turbulent northern waters in search of food and trade with different lands. This is a highly dangerous area to sail, not just because of the perilous waters, but because the seas contain many monstrous creatures, stirred up by the collapse of northern

Ulthuan centuries ago. Kraken, huge shark-like megalodons, behemoths and even the dread Black Leviathan are all known to lurk in the waters north of Ulthuan.

To survive in such waters, the sailors of Cothique must possess great skill, and the Elves that crew the light sea craft from Cothique are the finest in the world. Toughened from centuries of warfare against Dark Elves, sea monsters and Norse raiders from beyond the Old World, they excel in naval combat, and their nimble boats make deadly warships in times of need.

Yvresse

Yvresse is the land of mists. The mainland of Yvresse lies along the eastern coast of Ulthuan, but the realm also encompasses the islands of the Eastern Ocean. The mainland is a wild coastline, fringed by deep coniferous forests. The foothills of the Annulii march off into the distant peaks that tower dramatically into the clouds. This is the least densely populated area of Ulthuan. To those Elves from other realms, Yvresse is often considered unbeautiful, a bleak coastal realm, but to the Elves who call it their home the towering cliffs and soaring sea birds are sights as fine as any to be seen in the continent of Ulthuan.

Yvresse has only one major city: Tor Yvresse, a mighty metropolis as beautiful and grand as any of the Elf settlements of old. Sadly, its glory days are long past. Many of the old mansions are uninhabited and the great amphitheatres, once host to plays and masques, are silent and empty. The walls of the city are mighty and deep, but there are never enough warriors to man them and though the Warden of Tor Yvresse is a great hero, many wonder if the city could withstand another serious invasion.

Less than a century ago, Tor Yvresse was almost overrun by a vast Goblin horde led by the notorious Goblin Warlord Grom the Paunch of Misty Mountain. The innumerable Goblins ravaged a large tract of Yvresse and defiled scores of watchstones. Grom's army was only turned back at Tor Yvresse by the heroic efforts of Eltharion the Grim. Afterwards, the people of Tor Yvresse beseeched the Elf hero to become their new warden. Eltharion accepted, and has busied himself strengthening the land of Yvresse ever since.

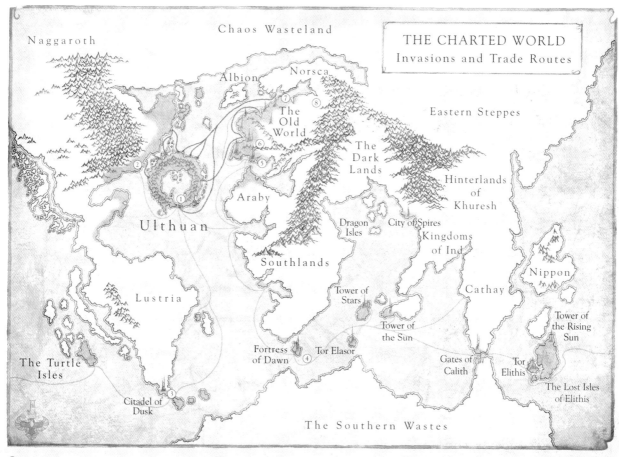

① Lothern – High Elf Port

② Arnheim – New World Port

③ Citadel of Dusk – High Elf Port

④ Fortress of Dawn – High Elf Port

⑤ Copher – Spice Port

⑥ Magritta – Estalia Port

⑦ Marienberg – Free Port

⑧ Erengrad – Kislevite Port

—— Invasion Routes

—— High Elf trade routes

THE ELVES OF ULTHUAN

THE CHRONICLES OF THE PHOENIX KINGS

Ulthuan is ruled by a collection of princes, princesses and mages, above whom preside the Phoenix King and the Everqueen. The relationship between these rulers is not as simple as the titles would suggest. The kingship is not hereditary, while the queenship is, and both the King and Queen maintain separate courts.

The Everqueen of Ulthuan is always the Queen of Avelorn. Her realm is the site of the principal shrine of the Earth Mother and she is regarded as the spiritual leader of the whole Elf realm. The High Elves place many of their greatest hopes upon her. The position of Everqueen is always taken up by the firstborn daughter of the previous queen, conceived during her year-long ritual marriage to the Phoenix King. After this formal marriage, they are free to go their separate ways. Both can take new consorts but only the daughter conceived from the marriage of the Phoenix King and the Everqueen can be the new Everqueen. Hence the Queens of Avelorn have always been the Everqueens of Ulthuan, forming an unbroken chain from ages past.

By contrast, the position of Phoenix King is elective. He is chosen from among the Princes of Ulthuan, one year after the death of the previous incumbent. Each Phoenix King is crowned during a holy ceremony, attended by the legions of the Phoenix Guard and the princes of Ulthuan, held at the massive pyramid Shrine of Asuryan.

The process of choosing the new Phoenix King is rife with intrigue and often emotions run hot during this fraught and delicate event. Traditionally the last thirty days of the year of mourning are set aside for the election to take place, however in practice the debate starts much sooner than that. Often the politicking starts long before the reigning Phoenix King has died. High Elves love intrigue, and never is the prize greater than when a new Phoenix King is chosen.

The greatest of Ulthuan's noble families will each seek for their candidate to be chosen as the new King, and they vie for the support and approval of their peers for their choice. Further to this, each realm in Ulthuan desires the new Phoenix King to be chosen from their land. So it is that rivalries are set aside or created to ensure that the agendas of the varying nobles houses are met.

For all the deception, manipulation and chicanery employed during the election process, it is almost unheard of for the tactics employed to escalate to violence or outright sabotage. Such actions are considered heretical for the Phoenix King is the anointed servant of Asuryan. Few High Elf nobles are so consumed with victory that they could believe, even for a moment, that the Creator God would ever approve of a King selected by the ruling council under such dubious and destructive circumstances.

The ceremony in which the new Phoenix King is crowned is a secret, mystical and dangerous affair, and it is only thanks to the ministrations of the Sapherian wizards that the new Phoenix King survives it at all. As the powerful mages utter incantations that will protect the supplicant, he is ushered into the fires of rebirth and there he faces his sternest test. Alone, the candidate must pass through the flames of Asuryan and in so doing he is reborn as the Phoenix King.

Only twice in the history of the High Elves have persons attempted to pass through the Flames of Asuryan without the consenting vote of the Council of Ulthuan and lived. The first was Aenarion the Defender, who emerged the first Phoenix King, while the second was Malekith the Great Betrayer, who in his insolence tempted the wrath of Asuryan. Malekith, unlike his father Aenarion, crawled forth from the flames burned and maimed and near to death. The cleansing fires of the Creator God left Malekith's body ruined and his mind broken. Such a fate awaits any who would presume to pass through the Flames of Asuryan without both the council's approval and the blessing of Asuryan, the Emperor of the Heavens.

A note on Chronology

Elves reckon time differently to men and Dwarfs. They are so long lived that their history is divided into 'Reigns' not centuries or millennia. Each Phoenix King's reign is considered to be a separate historical epoch, described simply by the manner in which the Phoenix King ruled, and the actions he carried out.

The Elven calendar, like that of men, has four seasons in it (Frost, Rain, Sun and Storm), and it is by this calendar that they measure time. In Elf records the reign of the Phoenix King comes first, then the year, then season and lastly the day. Thus V, 140, 3, 90 would equate to the ninetieth day of the season of the Sun, in the one hundred and fortieth year of the reign of Caradryel the Peacemaker.

Because a new Phoenix King is not elected until the previous has been dead for a full year, the 'missing year' is always considered to be the last year of the dead King's reign. No records exist concerning the dating system prior to Aenarion's reign (the day he stepped through the Fire of Asuryan being the first day of his reign), except that the Everqueens ruled alone, and the system revolved in some way around them.

For consistency, all dates described hereafter are also dated in the Sigmarite Calendar of the Empire.

AENARION

The Defender, 1 - 80 (Imperial calendar -4500 to -4420)

The reign of Aenarion the Defender began in a time of terror and strife. The nightmare creations of Chaos swept across the land. The warp gates, once used by the star-walking Old Ones to step from world to world, had collapsed, and a tide of uncontrolled magical energy swamped the known world. From these gates vomited forth gibbering legions of daemons, the lost and the damned. They marched forth to devour the world. The Old Ones had fallen, leaving their lost children to battle the Daemons alone.

The Golden Age of peace on Ulthuan came to an end. Borne across the seas on monstrous daemonic vessels, or excreted from tears in the fabric of the world itself, hideous servants of the Chaos Gods flooded forth. Against them, the children of the Everqueen had no chance, for they were unschooled in warfare and their magic was used only for peaceful pursuits. Entire villages were massacred, towns were razed and the High Elves pleaded to their gods for salvation.

Asuryan's Chosen

From the red murk of this terrible age emerged Aenarion, greatest and most tragic of all Elf heroes: a doomed champion, a fallen god, mightiest warrior in an age of constant warfare; the first, best-loved and most accursed of all the Phoenix Kings of Ulthuan.

A wanderer who had travelled the length of the world, Aenarion returned to Ulthuan in its time of need. Realising that the pitiful weapons of the Elves could not stand against the unfurled fury of Chaos he battled his way through the land to the shrine of Asuryan and there pleaded with the Creator God to aid his people. If the god heard, he gave no sign. Aenarion burned offerings, and the god did not respond. He sacrificed a white lamb. No aid came. Finally, in desperation, Aenarion offered himself, saying he would cast himself into the sacred fire if Asuryan would only save his people. As the god made no response Aenarion kept his promise and threw himself into the raging, white-hot inferno. Agony wracked his body. Pain seared his limbs. His hair caught fire. His heart stopped. Those who watched thought he was dead. Then a miracle occurred.

Aenarion refused to die. Slowly, painfully, he staggered through the fire. As he did so, his burned skin healed and his scorched hair re-grew. He emerged from the flame unscathed,

transformed by the cleansing fire. The spirit of Asuryan had entered him. There was a light about him that all onlookers could see. All were aware that he had become the vessel of a transcendent power. When he spoke, Elves hastened to obey.

Leaving the shrine, Aenarion led the Elves to war. Outside the walls he faced the howling Chaos horde. With a single throw of his hunting spear he slew the Daemon lord commanding the force, before taking up the Daemon's fallen weapon and butchering the rest of that abominable host, the power of Asuryan fuelling Aenarion's limbs.

The Elves took heart at the actions of Aenarion, and rallied to him even as the Daemonkind reeled from the shocking defeat. Caledor Dragontamer, the greatest Mage of the era swore fealty to Aenarion and together they trained the Elves in the art of battle.

With his army behind him Aenarion took the fight to the Daemons, slaughtering their champions and breaking their armies. Wearing armour forged on Vaul's Anvil, Aenarion was nigh untouchable, and his army of Elves and Dragons swept the Daemons before them.

In a brief respite in the fighting, Aenarion took the Everqueen Astarielle for his wife, and sired by her a daughter, Yvraine and a son, Morelion. All too soon though, the forces of Chaos attacked once more, and the silver horns summoned King Aenarion to war again.

From the riven warp gates, the Daemonic hordes attacked in renewed strength, and their numbers were beyond counting. Every Elf that fell was a grievous loss, and many were the heroes who died, but for every Daemon that was slain, yet more clambered over its corpse, eager to tear the Elves apart.

For a century the war dragged on, without respite or sign of victory and the Elves began to lose heart. Even the implacable Aenarion realised that there could be no victory, only a slow and inevitable defeat. It was Caledor, that wise and ancient Mage, who proposed a plan to thwart the powers of Chaos. Years of experimentation had taught him that the Old Ones' gates had collapsed, and it was these ancient devices that allowed the followers of darkness to invade the world. Caledor devised a plan to gather these energies and return them to the Realm of Chaos, to create a cosmic vortex that would drain the magic from the world, and save its inhabitants from Chaos. It was a desperate plan, with little hope of success, but Caledor and many like him thought a last desperate gamble would be preferable to the slow death the Elf people were enduring.

Aenarion opposed this, calling it the council of despair. Although in his heart he knew that the war was unwinnable, he was determined to put off the end for as long as possible rather than risk Caledor's plan failing. If news of a brutal

Daemonic attack had not reached Aenarion, he would likely have changed Caledor's mind entirely. The messenger, wounded and weary unto death, wept as he relayed to the Phoenix King how Astarielle had been slain, and Aenarion's children could not be found for the carnage.

The Sword of Khaine

Overcome with a titanic fury, Aenarion swore to kill every Chaos creature on the face of the world. Few who heard him doubted his resolution or his madness. Aenarion announced that he would travel to the Blighted Isle. Dread filled those who heard his words, for it could mean only one thing: Aenarion would journey to the Blighted Isle and there draw forth the Sword of Khaine.

A weapon of terrible power, the Sword of Khaine had waited, embedded in the great black Altar of Khaine since the beginning of time. As old as the world, it was the ultimate weapon, death made manifest - a splinter of the fatal weapon forged for the death god Khaela-Mensha-Khaine, capable of slaying mortals and gods alike.

All knew that to wield Khaine's sword was death, to damn your soul and doom your lineage and Caledor beseeched Aenarion to relent, but he would not be dissuaded.

Ignoring all warnings from mortal and immortal alike, Aenarion climbed onto the back of Indraugnir, the greatest of Dragons, and set off for the Blighted Isle. The journey was long and arduous and tested even the strength of the mighty

Indraugnir. Winged Daemons assailed Elf and Dragon alike as they travelled, trying to turn Aenarion from his path. The Elf gods whispered warnings in Aenarion's ear, but if he heard he paid no heed. Leaving Indraugnir just a few leagues from the altar of Khaine, Aenarion walked towards his fate. It is said that even the ghost of his departed wife pleaded with him to turn back. Though Aenarion loved his wife dearly, he hardened his heart and wrenched the great blood-dripping blade from the altar, sealing his fate, and that of his people.

A Mortal God

When he returned to the fray, his power was without match. None who stood before him could prevail for his arm was strengthened by the Creator God and in his hand he bore Widowmaker, and gods and Daemons trembled at his wrath.

Those Elves most embittered by the war against Chaos flocked to their king, and he created a kingdom in the north of Ulthuan, in the dismal land of Nagarythe. There, to the surprise of everyone, he took another wife, the strange, mysterious and beautiful seeress Morathi. Elves whispered how he had rescued her from the clutches of the Daemons of Slaanesh. To them was born another child, Malekith, who was to become the most hated of Elves. The court of Aenarion earned itself a dark and fearful reputation, such was the nature of its ruler, and the Elves of other lands were reluctant to go there. Tales of cruelty at Aenarion's court began to spread across Ulthuan. Even Caledor led his Dragon-riders south to his own land.

It is said that Caledor's departure angered Aenarion greatly, but the Daemons struck again before he could take action against his former friend. Such was the size and ferocity of the Daemonic attack, that it became obvious to all but Aenarion that the war was lost and the world was doomed.

The Vortex

Caledor, fully aware of Aenarion's madness decided that there was only one thing left he could do. Up till then he had respected his old friend's command abjuring him from creating the vortex. But now, with the world about to end in blood and fire, there was nothing left to lose. Caledor called together a convocation of the greatest High Elf Mages and they assembled on the Isle of the Dead to begin the great ritual. The mightiest Sorcerer Daemons of the Chaos host set to work to breach the spell-walls around the island.

With Caledor Dragontamer intent on performing the ritual, Aenarion was left with no choice. He assembled his forces and moved to defend the mages on the Isle of the Dead. At the centre of Ulthuan the two forces met. Dragons so numerous that their wings darkened the sky descended on the Chaos Host. On land and sea total war was fought between Elf and daemonic minion. The death agonies of monsters filled the sea with foam. Dragons plummeted earthward, killed by fatal spells. As the creation of the vortex began, the seas churned and a terrible wind blew from the north. The skies darkened and lightning bolts lashed the tortured earth.

While the battle raged, the High Elf sorcerers chanted the spell that would create the vortex. Chain lightning flickered. The world shuddered. For a moment all was calm, all was silent. Then the mountains shivered. Terrible energies pulsed between earth and sky. From the mountain tops bolts of pure power leaped to converge over the Isle of the Dead. While Aenarion and his outnumbered army fought, the sorcerers struggled to complete their ritual. One by one they died, the weakest first as the magic that they sought to control burned out their minds.

Aenarion, with only the faithful Indraugnir beside him, fought a bloody battle against four Greater Daemons of the Chaos Gods. It was a battle no mortal could ever win, yet Aenarion steadfastly refused to be beaten. The first to fall was the Lord of Change, its head cloven in two by a single blow. The Keeper of Secrets shattered Aenarion's ribs, but the Elf fought on, plunging the Sword of Khaine into the Daemon's chest. With a terrible scream it faded and vanished. Against the Daemon of Nurgle, Aenarion was saved by the cleansing flames of Indraugnir, that seared and destroyed the Daemon's impure flesh. Last to fall was the Bloodthirster, though it dealt Indraugnir a fatal blow, and broke Aenarion's arm, against the Sword of Khaine The Greater Daemon could not stand. Aenarion carved it in two.

Even as Aenarion defeated the four Daemons, the ritual was finally completed – or at least partially so. The High Elf sorcerers had succeeded in opening a vortex to drain away the raging magic, but were trapped within it, eternally keeping it open, forever trapped in their battle with Chaos.

His foes defeated, but his body ruined, Aenarion climbed wearily upon the back of the wounded Indraugnir and made once more for the Blighted Isle. Barely managing to complete the journey, Indraugnir crashed to the ground on the shores of that dismal island. Trembling from fatigue and the terrible wounds on his ancient body, Indraugnir gave one last bellow of defiance and died. Alone, Aenarion crawled back to the Altar of Khaine, He knew that should anyone take the weapon of Khaine, they could rule the world, and he thrust its blade back into the rock from whence it came. Then, it is said, he lay down beside the ravaged and torn bulk of his beloved steed and passed from that age of the world.

The immediate effects of Caledor's ritual were a series of magical storms, earthquakes and tidal waves that ravaged Ulthuan for three days. Thousands died as the shores of Ulthuan were swept clear by monstrous waves, ships were sunk and the sky was split by lightning bolts. When the storms abated, though, the warp gates were sealed, the Daemonic legions were gone and while Ulthuan was a land in ruins, it had a future.

BEL SHANAAR

The Explorer, 1 - 1669 (Imperial calendar -4419 to -2750)

After the disappearance of Aenarion the lands of Ulthuan were thrown into confusion. The Everqueen was dead, the Phoenix King was lost, and Caledor was imprisoned forever on the Isle of the Dead with the greatest and wisest of the High Elf Mages. The remaining princes of the realms convened at the Shrine of Asuryan, a year to the day after Aenarion disappeared, to elect a new Phoenix King.

There it was revealed that the first-born children of Aenarion, Morelion and Yvraine still lived. Sensing impending doom, their mother had sent them to be hidden in the Gaean Vale. They had been rescued from a Chaos attack by the Treeman Oakheart and his people. The Treeman had kept them safe in the wildwoods while war raged. Yvraine was ready to be crowned the new Everqueen. In her the spirit of Astarielle would live on.

The Second Phoenix King

The obvious choice for the next Phoenix King was Malekith, Aenarion's son by Morathi. He had grown to be a mighty warrior, a great sorcerer and an excellent general. But there were those who remembered the cruel days of Aenarion's court in Nagarythe and they doubted that any child raised there could be entirely wholesome.

Malekith said that he desired the kingship not for himself but in honour of the memory of his father. However, if the princes did not call upon him to serve, he would willingly swear fealty to whoever was selected. The princes thought this handsomely said and took him at his word. From their own number they chose Bel Shanaar, Prince of Tiranoc, an Elf who had distinguished himself in the war and yet was seen as a voice of peace and reason. Morathi shrieked her protests at her son not being chosen but Malekith calmed her and agreed that the selection was a good one. He was the first to bend his knee to the future Phoenix King.

So began the great days of exploration. Colonies were planted in Lustria, the New World and the Old World. Contact was established with the Dwarfs and a great era of trade and friendship began. Bel Shanaar, a seaman of wondrous skill, personally visited the new colonies and even ventured to Karaz-a-Karak in the Worlds Edge Mountains to swear the Oath of Friendship with the Dwarf kings. Malekith became his ambassador there. Thus, though none could yet know it, were sown the seeds of tragedy.

The Cults of Excess

The Elves spread and multiplied and wealth flowed back into Ulthuan. The cities became places of beauty and wonder once again. And though the folk did not realise, slowly, softly and insidiously, Chaos returned. It came in a new guise, that there were no defences raised against - it came back in the form of the Cults of Luxury and Pleasure.

Meanwhile Malekith heaped glories upon himself. He led armies against the Orcs plaguing the Old World and hunted down the remnants of Chaos. He searched for his father's armour on the Blighted Isle and stood transfixed before the Altar of Khaine. In the cold colonies of the northern New World, in the rubble of a pre-human city he found the Circlet of Iron, a talisman of awesome sorcerous power.

On his return, Malekith found an island in the grip of suspicion. The Cults of Excess were strongest in Nagarythe, his homeland. His mother the Lady Morathi had long been a devotee. Indeed, legend has it that she was one of the founding members, and their High Priestess. The Phoenix King was growing worried about the cults. Their excesses had already degenerated into the sacrifice of living beings and their evil nature was increasingly evident. The dark names of forbidden gods were increasingly associated with them.

Malekith appeared horrified by what he found in Nagarythe. He denounced the entire coven of pleasure worshippers, including his mother, and handed them over to the Phoenix King. Ingratiating himself further with the Phoenix King, he championed the hunt for hidden members of the cults. It seemed that cultists could be found in all levels of society. Nobody was safe from his scrutiny. Military action against the cults seemed inevitable. Malekith called Ulthuan's Princes to a Council of War at the Shrine of Asuryan. On the eve of the council the worst of horrors was revealed. Malekith claimed the Phoenix King was a secret member of a cult. Before Bel Shanaar could deny this, Malekith had him poisoned.

Now though Malekith had gone too far. No-one could believe that the King had been a worshipper of the cults. Certainly not the assembled princes who had all known Bel Shanaar long and well. Too late, the light of suspicion fell on Malekith. He and his followers already had the Shrine of Asuryan in their possession. The princes and their bodyguards were trapped within his grasp, and a secret treaty with his kin in Nagarythe meant an army of cultists would impose his will on the leaderless Elves.

Believing that all he had to do was crown himself and slay the princes, Malekith marched into the sacred flame, confident that like his father before him he could endure the ordeal. He was wrong. The flame of Asuryan would not suffer his polluted body to pass through it. His screams were so terrible that none who ever heard them forgot them till their dying day. Malekith was caught within the fire, his body terribly scarred and burned. Unable to pass through, he managed to cast himself back onto the side of the platform he had entered from.

With their leader on the verge of death, Malekith's followers took up their master's body and fled the shrine, leaving most of the Elf princes dead within. An age of tragedy and conflict was about to begin.

CALEDOR

The Conqueror, 1 - 550 (Imperial calendar -2749 to -2199)

Once more the Elf realms were plunged into turmoil. Malekith and his followers fled north to Nagarythe. Leaderless, the High Elves did not pursue. Frantic consultations were held between the few surviving princes, the Chief Priest of the Shrine of Asuryan and the Captain of the Phoenix Guard. It was decided that there was only one Elf capable of the task. The third Phoenix King was to be Imrik, who upon his succession took the name Caledor the First. He was the grandson of the famous mage of that name.

The Woodsmen of Chrace

Although he lacked his grandsire's gift for magic, Caledor was a great warrior and general. At the time of the murders in the Shrine of Asuryan he was hunting in Chrace. He was still with his companions high in the mountains when the messengers located him and informed him of the disaster at the Shrine, and the council's decision to elect him king. Moments later, one of the most famous events in Elf history took place. Malekith had despatched a band of assassins to slay the new Phoenix King and they arrived just after the messenger from the shrine, attacking immediately. There were dozens of them and they would have overpowered the future king had not a band of Chracian hunters happened upon the battle and intervened. These powerful mountain-dwelling Elves leapt among the Naggarothi assassins and cut them down, saving Caledor's life.

Afterwards, Caledor declared that he could want no better bodyguards than these hunters, and asked them to accompany him on his quest to the shrine. The hunters accepted, and thus were founded the White Lions of Chrace. Swiftly Caledor and his new bodyguard travelled to the inner kingdoms and took ship for the shrine of Asuryan. With full and proper ceremony he walked through the sacred fire and was accepted as pure by the god Asuryan.

Civil War

The legions of Nagarythe swept down from their grim realm, bearing the banner of Malekith before them. Caledor raised his own standard and called for all true Elves to join him in defence of the realm. Civil war engulfed Ulthuan and the colonies. In strength the two sides were equally matched. The Elves of Nagarythe were numerous and well-versed in sorcery and warfare, being those grim Elves who had followed Aenarion after he took up the Sword of Khaine. However, the new Phoenix King could call on the mighty Dragon-riders of Caledor and the legions of the Phoenix Guard.

Many Elf communities in Tiranoc and Ellyrion fell to the followers of Malekith, aided by traitors within their own gates. In Saphery, even then a realm famed for its sorcerers, Wizard Prince fought Wizard Prince, for there were many in that land who had taken their magical researches too far and into whose souls darkness had entered. Slowly, as the

followers of the Phoenix King gained the upper hand, these tainted mages fled to Nagarythe and lent their strength to Malekith and his armies.

The Witch King

Malekith himself recovered from his experience in the Shrine of Asuryan and called his armourers to him. With the aid of traitor Sapherian wizards and Hotek, a renegade Priest of Vaul, he forged a great suit of black armour which would lend strength to his withered and fire-blasted body. To the brow of its great horned helm was welded the Circlet of Iron. On the day of its creation he had his armourers fuse the suit directly to his body. After passing through the fires of Asuryan the infernal heat of their forges could not hurt him.

After that day those who looked upon Malekith shuddered, for he was a figure of dread. His armour was covered in vile runes which drew their power directly from the Realm of Chaos and hurt and baffled the eyes of all those who looked upon them. Upon his sword was the rune of Khaine, a reference to the blade wielded by his mighty sire Aenarion. Mounted on a Dragon warped by forbidden powers, he was ready to lead his armies to war. Ever afterwards, Malekith was known as the Witch King.

Fell he was and many were his victories, but to no avail. Time and again the new Phoenix King proved his cunning as a general. He sprang traps and ambushes on the Witch King's forces. He crushed them on the open field of battle. The White Lions and his personal retinue of Sapherian wizards protected him from many assassination attempts. In battle Caledor was unmatched, and in his fury he drove all before him. Wielding Lathrain, a magic sword of incredible power forged by the master smith Daith, Caledor hewed down entire regiments of traitor Elves. At each battle Caledor bested the champions of the enemy, breaking the resolve of the foe as he left their heroes broken and bloodied.

Finally at the field of Maledor, at the very entrance to the passes of Nagarythe, Caledor faced the Witch King himself in personal combat. Malekith, his Dragon slain by Caledor as they clashed upon the field, was forced to flee in a great black chariot drawn by Cold Ones. Leaderless and demoralised, the grandest of Nagarythe's armies witnessed the flight of their leader and the last of their resolve crumbled. As one they routed and the scattered survivors were driven into the marshes of the north kingdom.

After this, the folk of Nagarythe became ever more desperate, relying on the blackest of sorceries for their defence. Their evil nature became plain to see as they forged pacts with Daemons and dabbled in the blackest of sorceries. Thus the traitors came to be known as Dark Elves or the Druchii. But all their dark arts could not save them now that the full strength of Ulthuan was brought to bear.

The Last Gambit

The Witch King in his madness decided on a final scheme with which he could reverse the tide of the war. He gathered all the renegade magicians together and revealed a plan as insane as it was bold. They were going to undo the spells that held together the vortex and bring back Chaos to the world. The Daemonic legions would march once more upon the face of the world, but this time to the aid of their new allies - the traitor Elves of Nagarythe.

The Witch King and his followers would draw on the power of Chaos and become like unto gods themselves. So far lost to insanity were many of the Dark Elves that they readily agreed. One though, Urathion of Ullar, saw it for the world-destroying madness that it was. In the dead of night he slipped away from the Witch King's palace and brought word to the Phoenix King.

The Sundering

So began a last deadly conflict. The Witch King and his councillors began a terrible ritual that would unbind the vortex. The High Mages of the Elves attempted to stop them, but such was the awesome power of the Witch King's dark magic that he and his coven of mages slowly and inexorably gained the upper hand.

The heavens shook and the earth trembled. Once more an eerie glitter sprang up over the mountains and clouds of magical energies surged from the erupting peaks into the sky. In the far north of the world the Realm of Chaos churned and prepared to advance once more. In the camp of the Phoenix King, Caledor prayed to all the gods and to his grandsire to aid him.

At dusk as the sky shimmered with weird many-coloured lights, the Witch King and his followers began their final push. Daemons of Chaos came to their aid, and the last spells of the defenders collapsed before their onslaught. In the sky the triumphant laughter of evil gods was heard. Then, as the dark magic touched the Island of the Dead, at the very heart of the vortex, new players entered the game. Mighty figures clad in light sent the surge of mystical power tumbling back to Nagarythe. The trapped mages of the Isle of the Dead refused to let their work be undone.

The colossal power of the energies unleashed lashed Nagarythe. As the ritual reached its climax many of the Witch King's coven fell stone dead, destroyed by the eldritch power they wrestled. A storm of baleful magic raced over the land. Nothing could withstand the terrible forces unleashed. The island buckled under the titanic stress, and across Ulthuan earthquakes cast down cities and mountains.

Nowhere escaped the Sundering unscathed. A wall of water a thousand feet high smashed down on Nagarythe. The sea rushed in to cover all of the dark kingdom and most of Tiranoc besides. Thousands were slain, drowned by waves, buried by earthquakes or struck by magical lightning. The shock was felt as far away as the Worlds Edge Mountains and is recorded in the chronicles of the Dwarf kings.

The power of the Witch King was reduced but not broken. In those last hours as the seas rushed in to devour the land, the mightiest of the surviving sorcerer lords of Nagarythe cast dark and terrible spells upon their keeps. As the waves crashed round the hilltops, the wizards' palaces broke free and floated on the surface of the waves. Large as icebergs they drifted off to the north, steered by sorcerous power, carrying with them the remaining followers of the Witch King. Thus were created the infamous Black Arks.

The Dark Elves Flee

With the High Elves too weak to pursue, the Dark Elves retreated north in their Black Arks, to the New World where Malekith had found the Circlet of Iron years before. There the towers of the massive Black Arks became the cores of new cities. Around them a new, malevolent nation arose.

The Dark Elves named their new land Naggaroth after their old homeland and it swiftly become more sinister and evil than Nagarythe had ever been. A few Black Arks remained at sea, to patrol the storm-wracked northern seas.

For a century both sides nursed their many wounds from the terrible civil war. Soon though, there began a long period of sea warfare and skirmishing over the north of Ulthuan as the Witch King sought to gain a foothold on Ulthuan once more. Neither side had the strength to dominate and the Blighted Isle where the Sword of Khaine still rested changed hands several times. During this period Caledor oversaw the building of the fortresses at Griffon Gate, Phoenix Gate, Eagle Gate, Dragon Gate and Unicorn Gate.

Caledor's Fall

Caledor personally led the last expedition to the Blighted Isle and reclaimed it from the Dark Elves. It is said that he stood before the Altar of Khaine and for a moment the Blade called to him. He stood there for a time, head bowed and, in the end, simply said no.

Returning home from the conquest of the Blighted Isle Caledor's ship was separated from the rest of the High Elf fleet by a freak storm. It was attacked by Dark Elf raiders, who set the ship alight. For long hours Caledor and his crew fought off the Dark Elves, but gradually the Dark Elves gained the upper hand, and the Phoenix King realised that he and his remaining warriors could not win. Rather than fall into the hands of the Witch King's servants, Caledor jumped into the sea in full armour.

Thus passed Caledor the Conqueror. It was a bad end for a great king.

ALITH ANAR

The history of the Shadowlands is sinister beyond anywhere else on Ulthuan. During the Sundering, brother fought against brother and the Elves' island home was wracked by murder and deceit. Nowhere was this division more evident and the betrayal more grievous than the Shadowlands though, for Nagarythe was the greatest stronghold of the rebels, and any who did not support Malekith's rebellion were mercilessly attacked.

The fall of the Shadowlands

Aenarion's court, following his marriage to Morathi became a place of simmering evil, and it was here that the Cults of Excess festered in the reign of Bel Shanaar. When the Nagarythe threw their lot in with Malekith, it was from these decadent and perverse nobles that he drew most of his power. They were veterans of the wars against the Daemons of Chaos and many powerful sorcerers filled their ranks.

Not all the Nagarythe joined Malekith's rebellion against the true Phoenix King, however. Many High Elves had been appalled by the depravity ushered in by Morathi, and further sickened by Malekith's betrayal. These brave souls were the first to bear the brunt of the Witch King's assault, and their homes and their lives were quickly destroyed.

The greatest hero of Nagarythe, was Alith Anar – the Shadow King. A son of one of Nagarythe's noblest households, his family immediately joined the fight to protect the true Phoenix King and many loyal Nagarythe rallied to join him.

At the Battle of Dark Fen, the loyal Nagarythe stood before the mighty hosts of the Dark Elves. One of the first battles of Malekith's rebellion, the loyal Elves were outnumbered three to one and their foe were battle-hardened and cruel. Eothlir, Alith Anar's father was an expert tactician, and the Archer and Spear regiments who fought for him outmanoeuvred the Dark Elves for long hours. Hundreds of Dark Elves died crossing the fen, black fletched arrows claiming their lives, before the battle lines met. Crazed Dark Elf warriors tore into Eothlir's regiments, but even then it seemed that the loyal Elves could prevail. With his household at his side, Eothlir held firm.

The proud banner of the Anars fluttered just a moment longer before it was crushed beneath the immense bulk of the Dark Elf general's Black Dragon. As Eothlir was savaged by the mighty beast, a ripple of panic spread through the Elf army. As he fell to the ground, blood bubbling between his lips, Eothlir cried a warning to his son, Alith. Flee!

The Shadow Warriors

Few of Alith Anar's folk survived that battle, and they were harried through the fens and marshes for long weeks, until the Dark Elves grew tired of the search. When at last they came out from hiding, Alith Anar and his companions found their ancestral home a ruin, and scores of the elderly and innocent lying dead. There he learned that his grandfather, Eolaran, had been taken to the dungeons of Anlec – he was never seen again.

Alith Anar and his warriors swore terrible oaths of vengeance that day. They launched brutal ambushes on the armies of Malekith, butchering messengers, destroying supply chains and disrupting the flow of reinforcements. They joined many of the mightiest battles of the age, and it is said that Caledor the Conquerer thanked Alith Anar in person following the Second Battle of the Ellyrion Plains. There the Dark Elf army boasted scores of Reaper bolt throwers and the carnage they wrought upon the High Elves was terrible. As the Witch King's army advanced, however, the Reapers fell silent one after another – Alith Anar and his loyal warriors emerging from hiding to overrun their crews. The fighting was brief and one sided, the Shadow Warriors leaving the delicate war machines in ruins.

The Shadow King

When the Witch King and his mother, Morathi, fled Ulthuan into the west, the remaining few nobles of Nagarythe turned to Alith Anar to lead them. In the shattered groves beneath Dragon Pass they swore a pact of obedience to Alith Anar. Their land had been ruined, flooded by the madness of the Sundering and their reputation was in tatters. The Elves of other lands now viewed them as tainted – pariahs barely better than the Dark Elves they had fought against so courageously. That night each Elf from Nagarythe's great families took an oath of blood that they would not rest until they had destroyed Malekith and all of his followers. They became the Shadow Warriors, and Alith Anar was their lord, the Shadow King.

The Eternal War

In the wake of the Sundering, there were many Dark Elves still hiding in Ulthuan, and the Shadow Warriors busied themselves rooting out these remnants of evil. This was a task that Alith Anar and his warriors undertook with a vengeance and soon there were few of the Dark Elf reavers who did not know and fear his name. Each time his warriors slaughtered a Dark Elf encampment, his notoriety grew. None were ever spared, those that survived the fighting and were foolish enough to surrender or flee, were captured and then massacred as a sign of the Shadow King's passing.

After the Battle of Griffon Pass, Alith Anar captured seven hundred Dark Elves and had them nailed high upon the white cliffs overlooking the narrow valley, where they hung until they died, and then their corpses hung for years afterwards until their flesh rotted and their bones tumbled into piles beside the road. Such is the dark power of the place that these bones can be seen to this day, together with the red marks left by Alith Anar's iron nails upon the cliffs.

Later Alith Anar led his followers against the newly raised fortresses of Naggaroth. In the bleak lands of the northern New World, the Shadow Warriors became a serious thorn in the Witch King's side, harassing his ships, ambushing his warriors, and plundering his convoys. There was nothing the Shadow Warriors would not dare. It was said that Alith Anar once danced in disguise with Morathi at the court of the Witch King before stealing the Stone of Midnight from her treasury. He then outwitted the Witch Elves sent to hunt him down, tricking them into drinking poison mixed with blood before escaping into the wilderness.

The Aesanar

As to the final fate of Alith Anar none can say. His heirs have ruled the wandering folk of Nagarythe ever since, though none have taken the title of Shadow King which remains his alone. They are the Aesanar, the sons of Anar, and even the Phoenix King has never knowingly met nor spoken to them. These grim scions of the Shadow King still fight their eternal war against the Witch King and his followers, true to the oaths that their ancestors swore thousands of years ago.

Around the campfires of the Shadow Warriors, the true sons and daughters of Nagarythe still speak of Alith Anar as a living warrior, an Elf of the shadows, a mortal spirit of vengeance, bound to walk the earth until the Witch King is laid to rest.

CALEDOR THE SECOND

The Warrior, 1 - 598 (Imperial calendar -2198 to -1600)

The loss of Caledor the First was a grievous blow to the Elves. The old warrior had steered the realm of Ulthuan through its greatest crisis and held the kingdom together when it could have easily splintered and been conquered. He left the next Phoenix King with a strong army, a secure line of fortresses in the north and the most powerful navy in the world.

The Council of Princes met at the Shrine of Asuryan. Seeking continuity, they chose Caledor's son, who was to become the Phoenix King Caledor the Second.

Where his father had been wise, Caledor II was foolish. Where the father had been a great general, the son was rash and impetuous. Caledor II shared only one of his father's gifts: he was a mighty warrior. But to an Elf people desperate for stability, shocked to the very core by their sundering with their kin of Naggaroth, Caledor the Second promised a familiar hand at the tiller.

Rumours of the Elven civil war had reached the Dwarf empire in the Old World, but they didn't really understand the situation. Reaving and kinslaying were completely alien concepts to them, and no Dwarf would ever break his oath to his liege lord. Save for a few naval battles, the war had never reached the Old World. Secure in their mountain fortresses, the Dwarfs didn't give it a second thought.

The Witch King of Naggaroth hatched a new plot. As the Elves returned to the Old World in strength, trade between the two realms grew once more. Malekith had been shown the secret trade routes of the Dwarfs during his period as Bel Shanaar's ambassador, and he now used that knowledge to his own benefit. Dark Elves, garbed as warriors of Ulthuan, fell upon the Dwarf caravans, seizing their goods. Naturally, suspicion fell upon the High Elves.

King Gotrek demanded recompense from the Elves. When word of this demand reached the Phoenix King his reply was immediate and undiplomatic. He sent a message saying that the Phoenix King did not answer demands but granted pleas. King Gotrek sent a blunt reply to Caledor saying he made pleas to neither Elf nor god and demanded twice the recompense originally asked because of the implied insult. Caledor sent his ambassador back with his beard shaved off and said if Gotrek wanted compensation he should come to Ulthuan and collect it.

While all this was going on, agents of Naggaroth were abroad throughout the Old World stirring up trouble and further staining the reputation of the High Elves. Now it was a matter of honour. There could be only one outcome: war.

Dwarf armies marched down on the trading city of Tor Alessi (present day L'Anguille in Bretonnia) and laid siege to it. Gotrek swore an oath that he would have his money or its weregeld price in Elf blood, or he would shave his head. It was a mighty oath. His ambassador had already become a Trollslayer from the shame of having his beard shaved. The Dwarfs were determined that their king should not endure a similar fate.

Upon hearing of the Dwarf attack, Caledor was outraged. He instantly dispatched an expedition to relieve Tor Alessi. It was a mighty fleet and a great army. As they watched the towering ships sail forth, his advisors were dismayed because they feared that the despatch of such a force would leave Ulthuan almost defenceless. Caledor flew into a towering rage and dismissed their fears as groundless.

In the Old World the war dragged on. The fortress cities of the Dwarfs were virtually impregnable. The dour, stalwart Dwarf troops were quite unlike any the Elves had faced before. Displaying the tenacity and stubborness for which they have become renowned, the Dwarfs simply refused to give up or admit defeat, even when hopelessly outnumbered. This was not berserker bravery like that of the Daemons of Chaos or the frenzy of the warriors of Malekith, but outstanding courage allied to tactical cunning and consummate military skill.

For their part, the Dwarfs were astonished by the power of the Elf forces. They had judged the strength of Ulthuan by that of the least of its provinces. The huge armies of knights and disciplined infantry were not what they had expected. Still, in true Dwarf fashion, they were not about to admit to a mistake, especially to an Elf.

The war engendered a legacy of hatred and bitterness that was to last for thousands of years. In response to the beard-shaving incident the vengeful Dwarfs chopped down entire virgin forests to spite the Elves. Both sides fought till nearly their entire military strength was spent. Tired of their lack of success, Caledor II dismissed his generals and took command of the Elven host personally. It was his last great mistake. At the fourteenth siege of Tor Alessi, he and the warriors of his household sallied forth and charged right into the heart of the Dwarf infantry. Caledor II was cut down by King Gotrek, who snatched the Phoenix Crown from his corpse and took it in payment for the Elves' insolence.

The Dwarfs withdrew, claiming their honour was satisfied. Any petitions to return the Phoenix Crown were greeted with an invitation to come and plead for it. The first Phoenix crown remains in the great vault of the Everpeak to the present day, a source of festering hatred and recrimination between the two peoples.

Even as the Elves mustered a suicidal expedition to besiege Karaz-a-Karak, the world's most unassailable fortress, word came that the Dark Elves had invaded Ulthuan once more. The Witch King's long plan had come to fruition.

CARADRYEL

The Peacemaker, 1 - 603 (Imperial calendar -1599 to -997)

Once again, the Elves found themselves in the middle of a war without a Phoenix King. The fleets of the Witch King seized the Blighted Isle and retook most of the Shadowlands. Several Black Arks were beached to form the core of a new fortress city at the harbour of Anlec. From there the Dark Elves pushed south to besiege the Griffon Gate.

The High Elves were caught in the jaws of a trap, fighting a war on two fronts against two powerful foes. The Fourth Council chose Caradryel of Yvresse, who was as different from Caledor II as night from day. He was quiet and unassuming, an indifferent soldier but an able ruler. He made the hard decision to abandon the Old World. Faced with the implacable hostility of the Dwarfs it seemed to him foolish to maintain huge armies overseas, particularly with a more pressing threat to the Elven heartland. He abandoned pride, ordered the forging of a new Phoenix Crown and called the armies and Old World colonies home.

Among the haughtiest Elves there was a huge outcry. It seemed a gross insult to Elf pride that the Phoenix Crown should remain in Dwarf hands. Caradryel replied that he would rather lose the crown than the realm and continued with his policy. Many Elves, such as those in Athel Loren, refused to abandon their adopted homeland and stayed in the Old World, but most returned back to the island continent, seeking the protection of Ulthuan's armies.

Recognising his own inadequacy as a general, Caradryel appointed a succession of able field commanders to lead the High Elf armies. They scored many victories in the field. Tethlis of Caledor in particular established a brilliant reputation, lifting the siege of Griffon Gate and harrying the Dark Elves to within sight of Anlec.

Caradryel continued to oversee the long retreat from the Old World. He strengthened the forces holding the gateway fortresses and initiated a system of rotating units to the forts in succession so that the forces holding these valuable citadels would always be fresh and near to full strength.

For the rest of Caradryel's reign, sporadic war blazed through northern Ulthuan. More and more Dark Elves flowed in from Naggaroth. These were met by the disciplined, well-trained armies of the Phoenix King, many of whom were veterans of the wars with the Dwarfs.

Caradryel was the first Phoenix King to die peacefully in bed.

TETHLIS

The Slayer, 1 - 304 (Imperial calendar -996 to -692)

The Fifth Council chose Tethlis of Caledor, the hero of Griffon Gate, to be the new Phoenix King. Tethlis was another warlike ruler. He had learned well the value of preparation and organisation from Caradryel and he came to the throne with one aim: to force the Dark Elves out of Ulthuan. He followed through this plan with single-minded ruthlessness and determination.

Tethlis's heart was filled with a terrible cold hatred for the children of Naggaroth, for they had slain his family in one of their many raids. He fought not for honour or glory but to put an end to the threat of Naggaroth for all time. If the Witch King had started this long war, Tethlis was determined to finish it, and he might have succeeded had it not been for the decline in power of the Dragons.

During the latter part of Caradryel's reign, the Dragons had become increasingly rare. Many started to drift into longer and longer sleeps, waking perhaps once per century. The Elves needed to increase their strength in other areas to compensate for the raw power and savagery of the great beasts.

The first years of Tethlis's reign saw the assembling of new armies. Every Elf city was required to have a martial field where its soldiers could train and fight mock battles. Painstakingly, with meticulous attention to detail, Tethlis rebuilt the Elf forces to a strength not seen since the time of Aenarion. He never committed an army to the field without being sure that he could bring overwhelming force to bear and never fought a battle without being sure he could win it.

By relentless attrition he wore the Dark Elves down. Over the long centuries a series of massive offensives rolled the Dark Elves back through the Shadowlands and eventually culminated in the storming of Anlec. Victorious, the High Elves took no prisoners.

With Ulthuan secured again, Tethlis pressed on to the Blighted Isle. The largest Elf armada of all time was assembled to reclaim it. The seas around the Blighted Isle were swept clear of Dark Elf vessels and on the shore the Dark Elf host assembled to deny the High Elves a foothold. Thousands of High Elves were cut down by crossbow fire as they waded ashore. Ship-mounted bolt throwers returned fire and sent clouds of arrows arcing into the assembled

Naggarothi. The seas turned red with blood. Overcome with hatred, the Dark Elves charged into the water and a great mêlée broke out. Both sides fought with abandon, crimson water swirling round their knees. There was no place for skill. Warriors simply hacked at each other. The wounded were trampled and drowned in the shallow waves. Inch by bloody inch the High Elves fought their way onto the beach.

From the cliffs above the Dark Elves rained down a hail of fire. With his customary ruthlessness Tethlis had planned for this. While the Dark Elves fought on the beaches another force of High Elves had landed miles away. Silver Helm cavalry swiftly raced along the coast and came upon the Dark Elves on the cliffs. In the terrible battle that followed many Dark Elves were driven howling with hatred and fear off the cliff tops. Their bodies were broken on the rocks below.

The Elves now had a secure foothold to bring the rest of their army ashore. Swiftly they overran the island, driving their dark kinsfolk into the sea. Tens of thousands of Dark Elves were butchered until even the hardiest Elf captains' stomachs were sickened. They feared that their troops might acquire a taste for such butchery and become no better than those they fought against.

Many of the captains spoke against continuing on to Naggaroth, saying that they had achieved their goal, and that the loss of life was too great to continue. Tethlis insisted that they push on but first, drawn by some irresistible influence, he must make a pilgrimage to the Altar of Khaine.

On the Plain of Bones, the great skeleton-covered wasteland around the Altar of Khaine, Tethlis saw something glitter. Strangely drawn to the light he unearthed the dragon armour of Aenarion. Of the skeleton of Aenarion or Indraugnir there was nothing to be found. The armour he gifted to Auaralion, the great grandson of Morelion, Aenarion's son by Astarielle. This was virtually his last act as Phoenix King.

There are two versions of what happened next. Some records say that he dismissed the White Lions and the rest of his retinue, claiming that he wanted a moment alone to contemplate the blade that had done his people so much harm. It is said that a Dark Elf assassin emerged from his hiding place beneath the piles of bones and struck Tethlis down with a poisoned blade. Others say that Tethlis, determined to end the war with the Dark Elves, grasped the Sword of Khaine and that it writhed in his grip and started to come free, and that the king was cut down by his own bodyguard who feared the consequences of Aenarion's fatal weapon being unleashed once more upon the world.

No-one knows for sure exactly what happened. Scholars are divided. All that is known is that Tethlis died that day, and lacking his driving presence the High Elven armada turned back from Naggaroth.

BEL-KORHADRIS

The Scholar-King, 1 - 1189 (Imperial calendar -690 to 498)

With their people weary of war, the Elves of the Sixth Council selected Bel-Korhadris of Saphery to be the next Phoenix King. A wizard prince and a famed scholar, Bel-Korhadris believed that magic could shield Ulthuan from outside attack.

Thus began the great age of Elf scholarship. During the long reign of Bel-Korhadris the White Tower of Hoeth was constructed in a location deemed auspicious by geomancers. The White Tower took nearly a millennia to construct and required the skills of the greatest magicians and artisans of Ulthuan to complete. Mages inscribed grimoires of the most potent magic to be enshrined in its libraries. The tower was woven round with spells of illusion and warding to protect this treasured knowledge.

The Scholar-King founded the order of Loremasters at Hoeth. Every discipline from warfare to sorcery to alchemy and astronomy was studied there. It was during this time that the Sword Masters of Hoeth gathered to study the art of swordsmanship and protect the tower. From these studious soldiers emerged the continent-wandering order of master warriors who gather information and perform the errands of the Chief Loremaster.

Many famed scholars and sorcerors gathered at Hoeth and such exchange of knowledge occurred as has never been seen before or since. In the shadow of the needle-pointed spire thousands of the wisest philosophers debated about the most treasured knowledge and hidden lore.

Within the library a cadre of Loremasters began to inscribe the *Book of Days*, the great history of the Elven people on which all future histories would be based.

The reign of the Scholar-King is also notable for being a time of near unbroken peace. The Dark Elves of Naggaroth had been so weakened by Tethlis's onslaught that they were afraid to harry the realm. Bel-Korhadris ruled wisely and well and was loved by all. The Elves remember this as the start of a second golden age.

Bel-Korhadris died just after the completion of the White Tower and was buried amid its foundations amid great pomp and ceremony. Bel-Korhadris is the only Phoenix King not to be taken aboard the White Ships by the Phoenix Guard as a matter of choice. It is said that the ghost of Bel-Korhadris still haunts the crypts below the tower, occasionally assisting searching scholars.

AETHIS

The Poet, 1 - 622 (Imperial calendar 499 to 1120)

Bel-Korhadris was succeeded by Aethis of Saphery, the first Phoenix King who did not inherit an unstable kingdom or take the throne in the aftermath of a war. In his reign the long peace continued. The Dark Elves lay quiescent in Naggaroth. Many suspected that they were slowly dying away, fading into extinction with the passage of time and rumours abounded that the Witch King had finally died.

Aethis was a noted poet and singer. He gathered all the great artists of Ulthuan to his court in Saphery. Poets, dramatists, painters, sculptors, writers of histories and masques all found a place in his vast palace of carved jade. Prodigious amounts of wealth were spent on grandiose projects. The city of Lothern grew from a small fishing village to a great city to accommodate the increase in trade from the colonies and other realms. Contact was made with the old human empire in Cathay. Representatives of the Phoenix King visited the court of the Emperor of Cathay. Silk, jade and spices became valued commodities.

Secure in their strength, the Elves began to run down their armies and fleets. After nearly fifteen hundred years of relative peace under Bel-Korhadris and Aethis, memories of old wars and old enmities began to fade.

This was also the period when the High Elves came to realise that they were a dying race. Even during the long golden days of peace the population had fallen. The number of births had simply decreased and the great cities began to empty.

Once more the Cults of Excess began to spread, this time cloaked in a secrecy that made them even more attractive to bored Elf aristocrats. After a while the Sword Masters of Hoeth began to investigate the cults. Their findings disturbed the High Loremaster sufficiently for him to report to the Phoenix King. The Chancellor of the Court was revealed as a secret spy for Naggaroth. As he was unmasked he drove a poisoned dagger through Aethis's heart, and so the eighth Phoenix King was slain by a trusted friend.

MORVAEL

The Impetuous, 1 - 381 (Imperial calendar 1121 to 1502)

The Eighth Council chose Morvael of Yvresse, the High Loremaster of the White Tower, to succeed the assassinated Phoenix King Aethis. Morvael's first act after his coronation was to order a punitive attack on Naggaroth. An Elf fleet was despatched to the cold north and was swiftly massacred by the Dark Elves.

As the few survivors brought word of the defeat back to Ulthuan, panic back to spread among the High Elves. They had supposed the threat of Naggaroth all but extinguished, but now it seemed that the Dark Elves had merely been rebuilding their strength. A mighty Dark Elf armada seized the Blighted Isle and sailed on to Ulthuan. They retook the cursed city of Anlec and built a great fortress in the rubble. Swiftly they drove south and were stopped only after desperate fighting round the Griffon Gate.

Desperate for soldiers Morvael organised the system of troop levies that still exists in Ulthuan today, requiring every Elf to spend at least some of the year as part of a military force, and to provide wargear for himself. This system enabled the depleted population of Ulthuan to field mighty armies of citizen-soldiers well beyond what the declining population would suggest was possible.

Morvael was a sensitive, highly-strung soul, often troubled by terrible nightmares and dreams. He was forced to use the Sword Masters of Hoeth and other agents to seek out the devotees of the Cults of Pleasure and Luxury and it was his unpleasant task to sign many death warrants. Morvael emptied the coffers of the Phoenix Throne to build a new and mighty fleet capable of carrying the war to the Dark Elves upon the northern seas and halting the flow of reinforcements from Naggaroth.

Eventually the war reached its climax, and Mentheus of Caledor besieged Anlec with a great army of High Elves. Morvael remained in the Shrine of Asuryan awaiting the outcome of the battle. Every night he was assailed by ever more dreadful dreams. Some say these were sent by the Witch King to plague him. With every day that passed Morvael became ever more despairing and hopeless as messengers brought him reports of the army's casualties.

Eventually, weary unto death, Morvael abdicated his throne, simply walking into the flames of Asuryan and dying. On the same day that Morvael committed suicide, Mentheus was slain in the fighting at Anlec, although his army was able to rout the Dark Elves and drive them from Ulthuan.

BEL-HATHOR

The Sage, 1 - 660, (Imperial calendar 1503 to 2162)

The Ninth Council ended in deadlock, a tie between the factions that wanted a war-like king and a peacemaker. In the end a compromise was reached and Bel-Hathor, a wizard prince of Saphery, was chosen and crowned.

Bel-Hathor seemed an inauspicious choice; like most Sapherian princes he was something of an eccentric. Many of the other princes saw him as easily manipulable towards their faction's ends. They were wrong. Bel-Hathor turned out to be surprisingly strong-willed and wise. He refused all attempts to force him to order an invasion of Naggaroth. He knew that although Ulthuan could probably win a war in the bleak northern lands, the cost would be so high that the Elf realms would never recover. The numbers of Elves had so declined in later years that many of the cities were half empty and many of the lands abandoned. He was not prepared to gamble with the future of the Elf race.

Soon his attention was focused elsewhere. In the Old World the race of Man had risen from savagery to being the dominant civilisation in two short millennia. Two mighty realms dominated the northern portion of the Old World. The Empire, a loose alliance of city-states and provinces owing allegiance to its Emperor, and the kingdom of Bretonnia. Beyond the Old World was the northern realm of Norsca, home of the ferocious Norse raiders.

Norse longships had long troubled the coast of Ulthuan, slipping through the net of Elf warships. During the two hundredth year of Bel-Hathor's reign the Norse fleet led by Magnus the Mad attempted to take Lothern. Such a foolish endeavour went a long way to earning the berserk Norseman his honorific, however it was not to be the last, nor the greatest of the Norse raids. Within two centuries of Magnus' ill-conceived attack, the raids had intensified to the extent that the High Elf navy was ill equipped to cope. Scores of sleek High Elf warships had been lost in naval engagements and many settlements on Ulthuan's east coast had been pillaged.

Realising that the attacks would only become worse over time, Bel-Hathor called a convocation of all the realm's greatest mages and instructed them to guard Ulthuan's eastern approaches. After three decades of preparation the magicians enshrouded the island's approaches in a maze of spells, illusions and treacherous shifting shoals and mists. It became virtually impossible for Norse raiders to reach Ulthuan except by pure chance. Legends of these terrible sea routes reached the Old World and caused men to talk of the Elf-realm with dread.

The Norse were not the only men to dare the sea-routes to Ulthuan. Increasingly, the great naval powers of the Old World, the Empire and Bretonnia, also sent ships west over the ocean, seeking Ulthuan and the legendary golden cities of Lustria. The men of the Old World were determined mariners and eventually some of their ships found a route to Ulthuan. The Phoenix King issued an edict forbidding them to set foot on Ulthuan. He did however agree to let Finubar, Prince of Eataine, return to the Old World with them to study the new rulers of the Old World.

Finubar sailed to L'Anguille in Bretonnia and from there spent fifty years wandering over the continent. Because of the ancient feud with the Dwarfs, it had been a long time since any High Elf had set foot on the Old World. He was at once impressed and appalled at what he saw. The human realms were vast, teeming and populous. Men showed vast ingenuity in works of engineering and scholarship.

Finubar had expected mud huts and primitive savages. Instead he found mighty walled cities and disciplined armies, capable of fending off the Orcs and keeping the peace over huge stretches of territory. He saw that the humans were numerous and becoming more so, and that it was only a matter of time before they would eclipse the elder races. In addition he was fascinated by their crude vitality and exuberant culture, their energy and greed. He swiftly decided that it would be better for the Elves to have these people as allies rather than enemies.

In his travels he also came upon the lost Elf realm of Athel Loren. He was at once shocked and amazed by what he found there. The Elves of the old frontier province had taken a far different path from the High Elves, they had become one with their woodland home, as far removed from the High Elves of Ulthuan as were the Dark Elves of Naggaroth. Ever after they were known to their kin on Ulthuan as the Wood Elves. Though the Elves of Athel Loren were not unfriendly to Finubar, further attempts at rapproachment proved impossible and any ambassadors despatched from Ulthuan were treated with indifference, in the best cases, and in a few with outright hostility.

When Finubar finally returned to Ulthuan he was hailed as a great hero. The Phoenix King listened to Finubar's report and reversed his earlier edict denying the Men of the Old World access to Ulthuan. At Finubar's request the city of Lothern was opened to human merchants and Elf pilots were provided to guide the trading fleets through the approaches to Ulthuan. At such an invitation those races of Men who were inclined towards seamanship wasted no time in travelling to the Island Continent to see its wonders for themselves. Ships from the Empire, Bretonnia, Marienburg and beyond all flocked to visit the greatest Elven city.

Thus began a second period of explosive growth in Lothern. Prince Finubar watched his home city become the largest trading port in the world and was happy. The humans were astounded by the grace and majesty of Elf civilisation and well-pleased with the commerce that went on there. The Elves were content to have powerful allies in the Old World. When Bel-Hathor died peacefully of old age, Finubar was his chosen successor.

FINUBAR

The Seafarer (Imperial calendar 2163 to Present)

With the invaluable experience gained during his sojourn to the Old World, Finubar of Lothern seemed the prince best suited to understanding this new age. By temperament and experience he was equipped to deal with the race of Men, and as a native of Lothern he had grown up with an understanding of the worth of trade and a tolerant cosmopolitan outlook on the world. In accordance with Bel-Hathor's wishes, the ruling council elected Finubar.

In the one hundred and thirty eighth year of Finubar's reign, the Great Chaos Incursion began, and it looked as if the Dark Powers had returned once more to claim the world. A massive Dark Elf invasion swept out of Naggaroth and the Witch King himself returned to Ulthuan. For a time it seemed as if the Everqueen was lost and the realm with her. Then two mighty heroes, the twin brothers Tyrion and Teclis, arose to succour the realm and repel the invasion. By the efforts of the extraordinary twins the Dark Elves were driven off and Ulthuan was rescued from the brink of destruction.

Since then the world has grown darker. Despite the magical wards raised in the reign of Bel-Korhadris, Norse raids have become ever more numerous. A horde of Goblins led by

Grom the Paunch of Misty Mountain pillaged eastern Ulthuan. Dark Elf raiders have committed innumerable acts of piracy. The promise of a new golden age of peace has faded, and the Elves and their new allies have looked once more to their weapons.

For the Elves, the present is a time that holds both the promise of renewal and the threat of destruction. Their old enemies have grown stronger and they in turn have become weaker. Uthuan can still muster the mightiest fleet in the Known World and its armies are rightly feared by its foes, and yet the High Elves are a shadow of their former glory. Many on Ulthuan feel the greatest days of the Elves are passed.

Yet every year brings new opportunities to win glory and fight against evil. There are still mighty Elf heroes, courageous warriors and mages willing to stand against the Dark Powers and the mighty Dragons, though few in number, are turning restless in their long sleep. In the north the Witch King stirs once more and the Sword of Khaine haunts the dreams of warriors singing to their souls of forbidden glory. The High Elves still have a great part to play in the world before the final act of their long drama is played out.

TYRION & TECLIS

Among the High Elves, the names of Tyrion and Teclis are spoken with hushed respect. The fame of these twin brothers extends throughout Ulthuan and into the lands beyond. Prince Tyrion is the Elf general who turned back the Great Incursion of Chaos two hundred years ago. Teclis is the greatest sorcerer of this age of the world, a mage so powerful that spells and magical artefacts are named after him. Born into one of the oldest families of Ulthuan, the brothers can trace their line back to the doomed King Aenarion, first and mightiest of the Phoenix Kings of Ulthuan. It is their destiny to perform mighty deeds and shape the fate of kingdoms.

The brothers are as different as day and night. Tyrion is tall, proud and fair, a master of weapons, a match for the Dragon Princes of old in battle-prowess and skill. The chosen champion of the Everqueen of Avelorn, he is a warrior without peer and a foe without mercy. For two centuries he has stood between the Elves of Ulthuan and their many foes. He is a mighty champion, an unbreakable shield against the darkness. In him it is said that Aenarion the Defender has come again.

The age-old curse on the line of Aenarion affected Tyrion's twin brother Teclis more strongly. Where his brother is mighty, he is weak. Where Tyrion is golden-skinned and yellow-maned, Teclis is pale, dark and gaunt. Where Tyrion is

fair-spoken and noble-minded, Teclis is caustic-tongued and bitter. From birth he was sickly and consumptive. As a child, he was driven by an insatiable curiosity and showed an awesome gift for sorcery. He was schooled by the shadowy Loremasters of the Tower of Hoeth, who recognised in him great power. Within the precincts of the White Tower, guarded by magical illusions of great cunning, he learned the intricacies of sorcery, and rose to become a true master of High Magic.

The Dark Elf Wars

When the great incursion of Chaos came, destiny touched the twins. From the north the Dark Elves swept through Ulthuan looting, burning and pillaging. Allied with the servants of the four powers of Chaos they seemed unstoppable; the gigantic Black Arks of Naggaroth vomiting forth a wave of corruption onto the shores of the Elf lands. Ships of rune-woven red iron brought frenzied Chaos Warriors to Ulthuan and the Witch King of Naggaroth once more set foot on the land from where he'd so long ago been driven. Everywhere the unprepared Elves suffered defeat after defeat at the hands of their depraved kin. In the lands of Men things went no better. The shattered Empire, long a cauldron of factional strife, could not stand against the tide of Chaos. It was a time of blood and darkness; the world was ending in death and destruction.

Tyrion was in Avelorn at the court of Alarielle, the newly crowned Everqueen, when the Dark Elves came. The thunderous voices of their beasts filled the ancient woods. The shrill blast of their brazen trumpets echoed triumphantly through the heart of the land. Hurriedly the Maiden Guard of the Queen moved to meet the threat to their lady. A hastily assembled force of warriors was thrown into battle but to no avail. The Dark Elves were too strong and it looked as if the Everqueen, the spiritual leader of Ulthuan, would fall into their clutches. In desperation, Tyrion pulled her from her silk pavilion and cut a bloody path clear of the massacre, slaying any Dark Elf that got in his way. As they fled, Tyrion was stabbed by the blade of a Witch Elf, but disregarded his wound, and the two escaped into the heart of the ancient forests and disappeared. Word of the Everqueen's loss spread through the land and the hearts of the High Elves were filled with deep despair.

When the news of Tyrion's disappearance reached the White Tower, Teclis refused to believe his brother was dead. From birth, he and Tyrion had shared a special link and he was convinced that if Tyrion were dead he would know. He decided to leave the tower and seek him out. Using all his cunning arts he forged himself a blade and wove it round with deadly enchantments. Seeing that Teclis could not be dissuaded, the High Loremaster gifted him with the War Crown of Saphery and let him go. He sensed destiny in the youth and knew that the fate of the Elf kingdoms rested on his shoulders. Teclis was stronger now, the potions of the Loremasters had gone a long way towards giving him mortal strength. The High Loremaster hoped it would be enough.

Tyrion and the Everqueen fled through a land laid waste by war. The old forests burned as the Dark Elves took vengeance for their long exile. An army of Ellyrian horsemen was destroyed in the field by the Witch King's sorcery. The Princes of Caledor strove unsuccessfully to wake the last Dragons while the great navies of Lothern were driven from the seas by the enemy in a series of titanic battles. A Dark Elf army re-took the Blighted Isle and the Altar of Khaine fell once more into Dark Elf hands. Triumph followed triumph for the spawn of Naggaroth. Bitter defeat piled upon bitter defeat for the High Elves.

The Dark Elves were filled with glee at the news of the loss of Alarielle, but the Witch King refused to believe the rumour of her death. He insisted that her body be found so he could display it crucified upon his standard. Four assassins stood before him and pledged to know no rest till they brought him Alarielle's corpse. The Dark Elves sought the pair everywhere. Tyrion and the Everqueen often hid, crawling through the loam to avoid the eyes of Dark Elf patrols. As the Witch Elf poison gripped him, Tyrion grew ever weaker and more feverish, but with her land disrupted the young Everqueen could not find the power to save him.

The High Elves were reduced to fighting a guerrilla war in their own land while the servants of Darkness reigned everywhere. But now a new rumour filled all ears. A sorcerer was abroad and no one could stand against him. He was a pale youth who wore the War Crown of Saphery. Where he walked the Dark Elves trembled, for he commanded the powers of magic as if born to them. His words summoned lightning and cast down monsters and destroyed Chaos Warriors with a word. The Slaaneshi Champion Alberecht Numan challenged him to battle, but he and all his followers were in an instant reduced to dust. He intervened at the Battle of Hathar Ford and slew Ferik Kasterman's Coven of Ten - the most feared Tzeentchian sorcerers of the day. These were small victories, but in those days of darkness they gave the High Elves some hope.

Hope was what the folk of Ulthuan's many kingdoms desperately needed. The claw of Chaos held the island-continent firmly in its grip. From Chrace in the north to Eataine in the south, the Elf lands were overrun. Not even the waters of the Inner Sea were free of Dark Elf incursion. Ships were carved from the blighted forests with supernatural speed, and raiders moved as far as the Isle of the Dead before being turned back by the warding spells. Only in Saphery, around the White Tower, and by the walls of the mighty fortress city of Lothern were the Dark Elves halted, and even there things looked grim. Three Black Arks laid siege to the great lighthouse of Lothern, the Glittering Tower. By day and night spell blasts and siege engine shots battered the walls. The Phoenix King himself was trapped within the city, and it seemed only a matter of time before the entire land was devoured. With the Everqueen lost, the Elves had little heart to fight on.

The Darkest Hour

In the forests of Avelorn the hunt was closing in. The four assassins finally caught up with Tyrion and his charge, coming upon their camp by night. The wounded Elf Lord fought like a blood-mad wolf. Under the furious onslaught of his blade the Dark Elves died, but not before one unleashed a messenger familiar to carry word of their discovery to the Witch King. Howling with triumph the Lord of Naggaroth then sent forth his pride and joy, the Keeper of Secrets, N'Kari. With a roar, the Greater Daemon sped through the night to find its prey.

The Daemon found Tyrion and the Everqueen in the dark hour before the dawn, descending upon them like a falling star from the firmament. Once, the Everqueen could easily have banished the Daemon, but her power was much reduced even as her land was ravaged. Tyrion reeled to his feet, determined to sell his life dearly. With a sweep of one mighty fist, the Daemon dashed the wounded warrior aside. Looming over the Everqueen it reached out to caress her cheek with its claw.

Lightning suddenly split the night and the Daemon was knocked back. A frail-looking figure emerged from the forest. On his head was the horned-moon helm of Saphery and he swiftly took up position between the queen and the Keeper of Secrets. With an angry bellow, the Daemon rose to confront him. Teclis spoke words of thunder and a sphere of coruscating energy leapt forth, its touch instantly casting the Daemon back into the Realm of Chaos. Swiftly Teclis went to his brother's aid. Using all the healing lore he had learned in the White Tower he managed to summon Tyrion's spirit back from the brink of death's abyss.

Teclis guided the Everqueen and his twin to the shores of the Inner Sea. There they were picked up by a white ship crewed by the remnants of the Queen's Guard. This carried them to the Plain of Finuval where the shattered remnants of the Elf armies were assembling for a desperate last stand.

Charioteers from Tiranoc raced into position between Silver Helm cavalry and spearmen from Cothique and Yvresse. Ellyrian cavalrymen mustered beside the elite White Lions of Chrace. Griffon-mounted Elf Lords soared over the army. Sword Masters of the White Tower formed up alongside the Everqueen's Maiden Guard. When word of the Everqueen's presence was known, a great cheer went up from the army, and all the warriors gained new heart. But then a cloud of dust on the horizon announced the arrival of their enemies.

The Battle of Finuval Plain

That night the two armies camped almost within bowshot of each other. The watchfires of one force could be seen by the pickets of the other. In the Elf camp Tyrion and Teclis were greeted by their father Arathion. The old Elf lord gifted Tyrion with the Dragon Armour of Aenarion. This armour had been worn by the first Phoenix King during the ancient wars with Chaos. It had been forged in the searing heat of Vaul's Anvil and could resist even the fiery breath of Dragons. Out of gratitude for his rescue of the Everqueen, the Elves of Ellyrion presented him with their finest steed, Malhandir, last of the bloodline of Korhandir, father of horses. The Everqueen herself gifted him with a heart-shaped brooch which she had woven with enchantments for his safe return. In his mighty fist Tyrion grasped the runesword Sunfang, forged in elder days to be the bane of Daemons. So Tyrion was made ready for battle.

To Teclis, Alarielle gave the sacred Staff of Lileath. It granted him strength and power so great that he had no need for his enabling potions. He refused the offer of any sword though, preferring instead to use the blade he had forged with his own hands. He was now ready to stand beside his brother in the heat of battle.

The coming of day revealed the full extent of the Chaos forces. Endless ranks of Dark Elf crossbowmen chanted the praises of dark gods. A horde of Cold Ones croaked and bellowed in the chill morning light. Mail-armoured warriors brandished their spears. Witch Elves cackled and screamed maniacally. Beastmasters herded monsters into position. One entire flank of the Witch King's army was held by Chaos Knights and their bestial retinues. The Elves were greatly outnumbered and the situation looked desperate. From a blasted hill in the centre of that evil army, the black-armoured figure of the Witch King surveyed the battlefield, confident that victory was within his iron-clawed grasp.

Urian Poisonblade, the Witch King's personal champion, called out a challenge to single combat. Was there anyone in the Elf army brave enough to face him? Urian's reputation preceded him. He had been bred for battle by the Witch King himself. He was the greatest of assassins, the most relentless of slayers.

Arhalien of Yvresse was the first to respond. He was a mighty soldier, a veteran of countless battles. Urian cut him down as if he were a child. The Elf army moaned in despair and dismay. Next was Korhian Ironglaive, captain of the White Lions, the most renowned warrior of Chrace. Blows were exchanged faster than the eye could follow but to no avail – within minutes the proud High Elf lay headless on the plain. Then Tyrion strode forth.

It was a battle the like of which those present had never before witnessed. It was as if gods themselves made war. Sparks flew as blade clashed on blade. Both warriors fought in deadly silence. Again and again Urian's glowing black blade was turned by Tyrion's armour. Again and again the master assassin ducked the sweep of Sunfang. They fought for an hour and it seemed that neither would have the edge. Spells blistered the air around them as the Witch King sought to aid his champion. Sweat glistening on his brow, Teclis dispelled them.

Every witness held their breath. It seemed impossible that anyone could survive in the middle of that storm of blades. Then Tyrion slipped and Urian loomed over him blade held high. It was the opening that the High Elf had waited for. A quick thrust of his weapon found the assassin's heart. The host of darkness let out a howl of anguish and charged forward to overwhelm the lone Elf warrior and the Elf army raced to meet them. Malhandir reached his master first and Tyrion vaulted into the saddle then turned to face his foes.

The two forces clashed at the heart of Finuval Plain. The Dark Elves had the greater number and their allies were fell. The High Elves were fighting for their homeland and the Everqueen. They had the desperate courage that flowed from knowing that this might be their last chance to turn the tide. All that long day the armies fought with savage fury. Both sides were driven by the consuming hatred that their ancient civil war had bred. Flights of crossbow bolts, so numerous that they darkened the sky, were met by clouds of white fletched arrows. Monstrous Cold Ones were hamstrung by nimble Elf warriors. The horsemen of Ellyrion were pulled down by the foul beasts of Chaos. Spells crackled back and forth through the air. Blood mingled with the dust thrown up by the battle. Thousands died but neither side gave any ground. So great was the carnage that warriors fought over bodies of the dead and ravens feasted on the wounded trapped inside the mounds of corpses.

Right at the centre, Tyrion fought with the fury of an enraged beast. His great burning blade cut down foes with every stroke, and his shining mail turned the swords of his desperate foes. By himself he was worth an army. Where he rode the Elves took heart. Malhandir trampled Dark Elves beneath his silver-shod hooves. But Tyrion could not be everywhere at once and slowly the weight of numbers turned the battle against the High Elves.

The Defeat of the Witch King
At the heart of the battle, Teclis wrestled with the dark sorcery of the Witch King. Naggaroth's dark master had perfected his evil arts over long millennia and for the first time Teclis met a foe that was his match. Awesome magical energies were focussed and brought to bear. Lightning streaked the darkening sky. Terrible clouds, capable of stripping warriors to the bone, were turned aside by magical winds. Daemons howled and gibbered as they surged through the carnage. Teclis strode into the sky to better observe the battle. From the blasted hilltop the Witch King matched him spell for spell.

Teclis saw that the battle had turned. The size of the Dark Elf warhost was too great. It looked as if the Elves would be utterly massacred. Now there was nothing else for it. It was time for a last desperate gamble. He invoked the power of Lileath. His staff glowed and pulsed as the goddess fed him energy. Teclis sculpted the power into one bolt of titanic power and unleashed it upon the Witch King.

Frantically the evil one tried to turn it aside but could not. The blast descended on him, burning into his very soul. At the final moment he was forced to cast himself into the Realm of Chaos to avoid final and utter death. Freed now from the burden of dealing with the Witch King, Teclis turned his energies on the horde of evil. Spell after spell crashed down on the Dark Elves, hundreds died as lightning bolts and blasts of pure magic lashed them.

Malhandir brought Tyrion face to face with the Witch King's standard bearer and the High Elf cut down his foe with ease. Malhandir trampled the Witch King's banner into the mud. Seeing their Lord defeated and their standard smashed the Dark Elves fell into despair. Overhead the seemingly unstoppable Teclis rained magical doom down on them, whilst before them an unstoppable warrior clove through their ranks like a ship through the waves. Almost to a man that vast army turned and fled. Almost to a man they were cut down. The High Elves had won their first major victory of the year. The tide had turned.

Tyrion led the army south to relieve Lothern. Word of his coming gave heart to the High Elves. The tall warrior wearing the Everqueen's favour and his sorcerer twin became feared by their foes. The High Elf army fell on the besiegers of Lothern, putting them to the sword. The Phoenix King led his guard from Lothern to meet them. Caught between the hammer and the anvil, the besieging army was crushed. Outside the walls of Lothern, Tyrion and Teclis were greeted by the Phoenix King himself.

Within two days a great plan was conceived to drive the Dark Elves from the land. Tyrion would lead one High Elf army to Saphery to relieve the Tower of Hoeth. Meanwhile, the Phoenix King would drive north and engage the enemy directly. Word arrived from Caledor that the Dragons had been roused. At last, victory was within the High Elves' grasp.

The Gift of Magic
Just as the armies readied to set out, a battered ship limped into harbour. It was commanded by Pieter Lazlo, personal ambassador of Magnus the Pious. He bore a tale of woe from the Old World. The armies of Chaos had overrun Kislev and looked set to sweep over the lands of Men. Magnus had led the human defence of the Empire and, desperate for help, had sent to the Elves for aid.

The Elves knew that they could barely spare a single warrior from their forces and yet they knew that if Mankind failed then the forces of Chaos in the Old World would be free to aid the Dark Elves.

Hearing once more the call of destiny, Teclis volunteered to go to the aid of Mankind. Yrtle and Finreir, two of his old comrades from the Tower of Hoeth agreed to go with him. It was all that could be done. The two brothers parted at the docks in Lothern. It was a bleak farewell. Neither knew if they would ever see each other again. Teclis took to his ship. Tyrion rode away with his army.

Now leading the Elf army, Tyrion proved to be every bit as skillful a general as he was a warrior. His surprise attack routed the Chaos forces in the woods around the White Tower. Joined by a contingent of Sword Masters, his army marched on into southern Avelorn to reclaim the Everqueen's land. There the Dark Elves had been demoralised by the Witch King's defeat and hounded relentlessly by guerrilla forces. Tyrion drove them out of the woods and into the hills of southern Chrace.

In this mountainous land a savage war of ambush and counter-ambush was fought. But the Phoenix King had lent Tyrion the services of a unit of White Lions and these bold warriors' knowledge of their homeland was to prove invaluable. In the year 2303, exactly two years after the invasion began, the Phoenix King and Tyrion met at Tor Achare, the capital of Chrace. The Dark Elves had been driven from the mainland of Ulthuan. The war was all but over, although bitter fighting was to rumble on in the islands for many decades.

In the Old World, Teclis and his companions arrived at the court of Magnus the Pious, where Teclis's wise advice and mighty sorcery soon made him an invaluable counsellor. The influence of the three High Elf Mages changed the course of the war. They taught some simple battle-spells to the human hedge-wizards and these, combined with their own command of awesome forces, aided in many victories. The Mages proved willing to spill their own blood in defence of the lands of man. Teclis and Finreir both took many wounds; Yrtle fell in battle and was buried with great honour. But it was after the war, when Magnus had driven the enemy from the land and he'd been hailed as the new Emperor, that he performed what was to be his most significant act.

Magnus requested that Finreir and Teclis teach the full secrets of magic to men. He had seen how instrumental it had been in holding back the tide of Chaos and wanted to add yet another weapon to Mankind's arsenal. At first Finreir resisted. Elves and Men had come to blows in the past and would surely do so again. Teclis took the long view. He argued that by helping Men protect themselves against Chaos they would create an invaluable bulwark against the forces of darkness. Eventually Teclis's view prevailed and the Colleges of Magic were established. Teclis himself taught the first human students and more than twenty years passed before he returned home. Through his work as a teacher, he grew fond of the race of Men and saw in it the possibility and the threat that in time it might far exceed the declining race of Elves.

The two brothers met again at their ancestral home in the year 2326 when Teclis returned for their father's funeral. It was a sad moment but the two embraced joyously. Tyrion was now a warrior of incomparable valour and skill at arms and had become the chosen Champion of the Everqueen, second only to the Phoenix King among the defenders of Ulthuan. Teclis planned to return to the Empire to continue his work, and to keep a closer eye on the developing race of mankind, but word came that the High Loremaster of the White Tower had died and the council of Saphery offered Teclis his position. Teclis could not refuse such an honour and so returned to the Tower of Hoeth.

Since the days of the Great War against Chaos, the two brothers have been active in the defence of Ulthuan. Tyrion led the army that defeated Erik Redaxe's army of Norse raiders and twice led expeditions to the Blighted Isle to reclaim the Altar of Khaine from the Dark Elves. Both times he drove the spawn of Naggaroth off but always they return. When not leading the armies to war he dwells at the court of the Everqueen and keeps the peace in Avelorn, slaying marauding monsters and hunting down bands of Beastmen and Goblins.

Teclis probes the ancient mysteries of sorcery at the White Tower. Often his researches demand that he visit the far corners of the world. He has ventured as far afield as Cathay and Lustria and has aided armies both human and High Elf against the forces of evil.

ELTHARION

In the 260th year of the reign of the current Phoenix King, Finubar the Seafarer, Eltharion became the first High Elf ever to lead a successful raid against Naggarond and return alive.

The High Elf army was small but Eltharion force-marched his followers through the bleak landscape of Naggaroth. He took many Dark Elf garrisons by surprise and razed them to the ground. On his Griffon, Stormwing, Eltharion himself rode down those that fled, and ensured that not one Dark Elf escaped to send word to the Witch King. Thousands of Dark Elf warriors were cut down by the disciplined High Elf Spear regiments who advanced across the landscape. Patrols of Ellyrion Reavers worked in concert with Shadow Warrior bands, ambushing enemy messengers and sowing terror and confusion deep into Dark Elf territory.

When at last Eltharion's army reached Naggarond, the boldest Elves clad themselves in captured garb and entered the city, opening the gates from within. The waiting High Elves poured into the city and ran riot, burning buildings and slaying all they found. It was as they prepared to fall back that disaster struck and Eltharion was wounded by the blade of a Witch Elf. He struck back beheading his attacker, but the damage was done – the envenomed sword had left its poison in his blood. The raid had been a success and the High Elf force escaped to Ulthuan with minimal losses, but by the time they docked at Chrace, Eltharion was near death.

The night of their return, the High Elves pitched camp near the shore, for the journey had been arduous. None amongst them had the skill to counter the Dark Elf venom, and it was with heavy hearts that Eltharion's most trusted lieutenants laid him in his tent, knowing he would be dead by morning.

Moranion's Message

During the night, Eltharion stirred from his fevered sleep. Opening his eyes dreamily he saw a pale apparition, and with horror realised that the ghostly form was none other than his father Moranion. The shadowy figure was bloodied and mangled by blade-marks and arrows, and Eltharion knew his father was dead.

The spirit spoke in hollow tones, telling him that their ancestral home of Athel Tamarha had been destroyed and its lands defiled. He warned his son that the Goblin Warlord Grom was abroad in Ulthuan. A terrible foe, with a shaman of frightful power at his command, Grom and his vast army of Goblins was overwhelming all in his path. In their ignorance they had defiled every watchstone between Athel Tamarha and Tor Yvresse. The magical energies they normally contained were wracking the land and the Phoenix King's armies were too far away to act. If the watchstone of Tor Yvresse were to fall too, then devastation on a scale not seen since the Sundering would be unleashed.

When Eltharion fully awoke, miraculously cured of the Dark Elf poison, the ghost was gone, but looking down he saw the Fangsword, ancient heirloom of his family, resting where his father's spirit had been. He knew his destiny was to avenge his father and his home. He arose from his bed and grasped the sword, feeling new strength flow into him as he lifted it.

The Siege of Tor Yvresse

In the morning the astounded High Elf commanders found their Lord awake and alert, pale and wan but strong. His face was dark as he told them of his vision and his quest. He bade them return to their ships. With all the speed they could muster they sailed for Yvresse. Upon arrival they found the great city in flames, Goblins and Orcs, led by Grom raged through the streets. Outnumbered regiments of High Elves bravely fended off hordes of Goblins. No matter how hard they fought though, they were losing, street by street - every Goblin that fell was instantly replaced, while the outnumbered Elves had no reinforcements. Above the blazing buildings, the Goblin shaman flew upon a great Wyvern, blasting the city with foul magic.

As his ship drew into the harbour, Eltharion briefed his warriors. Victory lay in securing the Warden's Tower and the watchstone of Tor Yvresse. He entrusted his most loyal soldiers with this task and they swore to complete it. Before the first Eagle ship had reached the docks, Eltharion took to the back of his mighty Griffon Stormwing and soared high above Tor Yvresse. Hundreds of Elf warriors followed their master's example, and rushed ashore to join the fight.

Far above, Eltharion charged directly at the Shaman, who saw him almost too late. Through strength of will alone, Eltharion deflected the lethal magic that the Shaman propelled at him, as Stormwing raked and clawed at the startled Wyvern. For long minutes the pair circled one another, the Shaman unleashing a hail of spells that bludgeoned the Elf lord and left him reeling. For a moment it looked as though the Goblin would prevail, and he prepared a final, deadly spell to finish off Eltharion, when suddenly he halted mid-spell. Eltharion's warriors had seized the Warden's Tower and made the Invocation of Ending - temporarily becalming the Winds of Magic. Seizing his chance, Eltharion attacked and took the Shaman's head off with a single stroke of his blade. With that act the Greenskin attack faltered and Eltharion's veteran regiments swept the Goblins from the city. Grom first tried to rally his fleeing army, but after a moment's thought, shrugged and joined the fleeing masses.

Eltharion did not stop to savour the victory but instead went with four of his bravest warriors to the Warden's Tower. There they wrestled with the power of the watchstone, seeking to stablise the vortex. Nobody knows what took place in there, but in the morning, only Eltharion emerged alive, his face more grim than ever.

The following morning not even the sunrise nor the cheering crowds of the victorious High Elves could force a smile from him. He was elected Warden of Tor Yvresse in recognition of his feats but from then on the haunted hero was forever known as Eltharion the Grim.

THE BOOK OF DAYS

The Golden Time

These years are not dealt with in the Chronicle of the Phoenix Kings. During this time the Everqueen ruled Ulthuan from Avelorn and many realms were founded by adventurers departing from that primeval land. The time ends with the coming of Chaos and the years of violence that then ensued.

Aenarion, the Defender

(Imperial Calendar -4500 to -4420)

Aenarion passes through the sacred flame and then defends the Shrine of Asuryan against the Chaos Horde of Morkar. **1**

2 Aenarion arrives in Caledor and is recognised as the chosen of Asuryan by Caledor Dragontamer. The great dragon Indraugnir becomes Aenarion's steed. They fly to Vaul's Anvil where the Dragon Armour of Aenarion is forged along with many weapons that will eventually become heirlooms of the great Elf noble families. Technically, the rank of Prince in present day Ulthuan belongs to anyone who can show possession of one of these ancient weapons.

The war against Chaos begins in earnest as the Elf Dragonriders from Caledor take the fight to the enemy. **3**

The forces of Chaos are driven back for a time and a fragile peace descends on Ulthuan. Aenarion marries the Everqueen Astarielle and two children, Yvraine and Morelion, are born to them. **21**

The Weapons of the Princes

By Aenarion's command the Priests of Vaul forged weapons to aid the High Elves in the war against the Daemons. These weapons were amongst the mightiest magical items ever wrought, and at a time of great despair, they brought renewed hope to the beleaguered High Elves. Although a great many of these treasured artefacts have since been lost in battle, some few remain, like the swords Sunfang and Chabrael or the fabled Spear of Twilight.

Morelion's Line

History fails to accurately record exactly why Morelion was not considered as a potential successor to the Phoenix Throne. Morelion, it appears contented himself by taking possession of several of the mightiest heirlooms created for the wars against the Daemons and retiring to Avelorn where he could ensure the continued safety of his sister, Yvraine.

The forces of Chaos attack Avelorn. The Everqueen is slain and her children believed lost. In fact they are in the care of the Treeman Oakheart. Wracked with grief, Aenarion flies to the Blighted Isle and draws the Sword of Khaine. Armed with this terrible weapon he is all but invincible for a time. **30**

Aenarion rescues the witch Morathi from a Slaaneshi warband. They make court in Nagarythe. **39**

Caledor Dragontamer concludes that the only way to stop Chaos is to drain the Winds of Magic from the world. He starts repairing and expanding the ancient network of standing stones which has stood upon Ulthuan since the dawn of time. **40**

42 Morathi bears Aenarion a child, Malekith, the future Witch King of Naggaroth.

79 The Battle of the Isle of the Dead. At this epic battle Caledor Dragontamer creates the magical Vortex. Aenarion suffers a mortal wound and as his last act flies to the Blighted Isle and drives the Sword of Khaine back into the altar. Aenarion's body is never found.

Bel Shanaar, The Explorer
(Imperial Calendar -4419 to -2750)

The coronation of Bel Shanaar marks the end of the war with Chaos and the start of the great period of rebuilding that sees the rise of Tiranoc to pre-eminence among the Elf realms.

1

The foundation of the first colonies in the New World, on the east coast. Malekith defeats the Orc warlord Gritok Redfang and saves the city of Athel Toralien.

255

The Elves land in the Old World. Malekith befriends the Dwarf King Snorri Whitebeard and together the armies of Dwarfs and Elves begin to drive the remnants of Chaos from the lands. As the colonies prosper wealth begins to flow back to Ulthuan.

300

The Cult of Pleasure begins its slow spread through Nagarythe and across all Ulthuan.

1000

The Cults of Excess

The Cults of Excess, as the many deviant groups associated with the worship of forbidden Elven deities are collectively known, have remained a constant thorn in the side of the High Elves, even after the Sundering. Most commonly known of these proscribed sects are the Cult of Luxury and the Cult of Pleasure. The Cult of Pleasure in particular is renowned for its wanton violence and cruelty, something that has earned it the enmity of all right-minded High Elves.

Bel Shanaar himself visits the newly founded Dwarf city of Karaz-a-Karak and signs the pledge of eternal friendship between Dwarfs and the Elves. Malekith stays on as ambassador and remains on friendly terms with the Dwarf kings.

1580

Malekith begins his great period of wandering around the world in search of magical artefacts of elder times.

1630

In the northern wasteland Malekith finds the Circlet of Iron in the ancient ruined city of Vorshgar.

1644

Malekith returns to Ulthuan and denounces his own mother as a worshipper of the Cult of Pleasure.

1645

The massacre at the Shrine of Asuryan. Bel Shanaar is assassinated. Malekith is burned by the sacred flame and horribly mutilated. Later that year his assassins try to kill the future Phoenix King Caledor I who is rescued by a band of Chracian hunters, the ancestors of the White Lions.

1668

Malekith the Great

The valourous acts carried out by Malekith during the first sixteen hundred years of Bel Shanaar's reign were the stuff of legend, and only an act of perfidy as vile as Malekith's ultimate betrayal could ever erase the sheer heroism and gallantry that it must have taken to perform them. Even now High Elf scholar-historians fail to comprehend how Malekith the Great, hero of Elf and Dwarf alike could sink so low as to carry out murders and butchery upon his own people, and threaten the destruction of the world. Though once the name of Malekith the Great was shouted by enthusiastic young Elves, and sung of in poems and lays, "The Great" is now an epithet that is as dead as it is inappropriate.

The Massacre at the Shrine

Malekith's treachery within the shrine of Asuryan cost many of the finest leaders in Ulthuan their lives. An ancient edict forbids the shedding of blood within the Shrine, and so Malekith's surprise was total. The unarmed princes of Ulthuan were ruthlessly butchered by Malekith and his treacherous followers and only three of the princes loyal to the Phoenix Crown survived. Only steadfast bravery on the part of the High Elves, coupled with Malekith's rejection by the Flames of Asuryan, allowed any to survive at all.

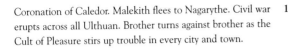

Caledor, The Conqueror
(Imperial Calendar -2749 to -2199)

1 Coronation of Caledor. Malekith flees to Nagarythe. Civil war erupts across all Ulthuan. Brother turns against brother as the Cult of Pleasure stirs up trouble in every city and town.

4 The Battle of Dark Fen.

10 The renegade wizard princes flee Saphery and join Malekith. Hotek, a heretic priest of Vaul, steals the sacred hammer from Vaul's Anvil and makes his way to Nagarythe.

13 Malekith is sealed within his great black armour and is hailed as the Witch King. The intensity of the war increases.

25 Caledor defeats the Witch King at the Battle of Maledor. The Witch King flees and decides to implement his master plan.

26 The Sundering. As a result of the Witch King's interference with the Vortex much of northern Ulthuan is sunk. The renegade wizards raise the Black Arks and depart to the north to found the Dark Elf kingdom of Naggaroth. There is little the High Elves can do to stop them at this point. Tiranoc is lost beneath the waves and the cataclysmic unleashing of energies devastates the land. The Elves begin to rebuild their shattered land. Contact is lost with the Old World colonies.

119 A Dark Elf expedition returns to Ulthuan and hostilities resume. Caledor reorganises the High Elf army for defence and begins the building of the Gateway fortresses in the northern passes.

150 Griffon Gate, the Unconquered Fortress, is finally completed. It is the first of a series of massive strongholds that will eventually guard the approaches to the Inner Lands. The war rages on as the Dark Elves seek to gain access to the Inner Lands and conquer the Holy Shrines. The High Elves resist them.

324 The dragon ship *Indraugnir*, armed with the magically forged starblade ram, sinks the *Palace of Joyous Oblivion* near the Blighted Isle. This is the first time a Black Ark has ever been sunk and marks the beginning of the High Elves' naval ascendancy over their dark kindred.

530 The Elves finally succeed in driving the last Dark Elves from northern Ulthuan and begin to sweep the northern seas clear of their ships.

532 Caledor orders the first of the ill-starred expeditions to recapture the Blighted Isle.

549 The High Elves take the Blighted Isle. Caledor does not draw the Sword of Khaine even though it would give him the power to defeat the Witch King. On his way home a great tempest separates his flagship *Indraugnir* from the rest of the fleet. Sails torn, driven to the very coast of Naggaroth, the ship is overwhelmed by Dark Elf reavers. Caledor throws himself into the sea rather than be captured.

Caledor II, The Warrior
(Imperial Calendar -2198 to -1600)

1 An uneasy peace settles over Ulthuan. The survivors from Tiranoc and what was once Nagarythe start rebuilding their lands. The remaining Elves of Nagarythe, which has become known as the Shadowlands, take up a wandering, nomadic life shunning the trappings of civilisation.

10 Contact is re-established with Dwarfs. Trade returns.

193 Dark Elf raids begin against Dwarf trading caravans.

198 Dwarf protests are ignored by Caledor II. Increasing acrimony enters relations between the two races.

201 The War of the Beard begins. This will eventually exhaust the strength of both empires and lead to ages of bitter feuding. There are many periods of peace where both sides claim victory.

224 Caledor II personally kills Snorri Halfhand, King Gotrek's son, before returning to Ulthuan in time for the hunting season.

230 Morgrim, Snorri's cousin, kills Caledor's brother Imladrik.

250 The Dwarfs destroy the Elf colony of Athel Maraya.

596 Caledor II comes to the Old World to supervise the defeat of the Dwarf kings.

597 Caledor II killed by Gotrek Starbreaker. The Phoenix Crown is lost. Announcing their victory the Dwarfs retreat to the mountains and refuse to fight any more. As the Elf host is assembled for a suicidal attack on Karaz-a-Karak, news reaches them that the Witch King has once again invaded Ulthuan.

Caradryel, The Peacemaker
(Imperial Calendar -1599 to -997)

1 — The Black Arks *Citadel of Ecstatic Damnation* and *Jade Palace of Pain* are beached to become the core of the fortress of Anlec in the Shadowlands. This will provide the Dark Elves with a base from which to launch many massive attacks.

10 — Caradryel orders the recall of the Elf armies from the Old World to combat this new threat. Demoralised by the long war against the Dwarfs, the Elves are in no position to deal with the resurgent Naggarothi.

17 — Aevin Thornchanter turns himself into a narinocha plant while attempting to harness the Wind of Ghyran.

98 — The last Elf army departs from the Old World, leaving behind a few hardy colonists who refuse to go. What will become the Wood Elf realm of Athel Loren is founded.

102 — Caradryel introduces the system of rotating units to the Gateway fortresses so that the garrisons are always at full strength. Intermittent war rages across Ulthuan once more as the Dark Elves consolidate their hold on the northern lands.

602 — Caradryel dies peacefully.

Forging of a new Phoenix Crown
With Caledor II dead, and the Phoenix Crown lost to Gotrek Starbreaker, Caradryel insisted on having a new Phoenix Crown forged. The task of forging this legendary item fell to the Priests of Vaul, who undertook the work with all diligence. The new Phoenix Crown took nearly a century of ceaseless labour to complete. It is interesting to note that, according to High Elf records, only Caledor II possessed the legendary arrogance to wear the Phoenix Crown into battle - no other Phoenix King before or after has attempted this.

Tethlis, The Slayer
(Imperial Calendar -996 to -692)

3 — The first Dragons begin their long sleep.

10 — Tethlis launches the Scouring, a great drive north that will culminate in the slaying of every Dark Elf in Ulthuan.

74 — The Battle of Grey Canyon. A massive army of Dark Elves is caught by surprise and destroyed while camped in a hidden valley in the Shadowlands.

219 — Dark Elf Shades and Assassins ambush Tethlis and his bodyguard while travelling north from the Phoenix Gate. No Dark Elves survive the encounter. Tethlis is unharmed.

5 Formal military training for Elf regiments begins.

50 Naggarothi counter-offensive reaches Griffon Gate and is caught in a carefully prepared trap.

167 Alaesir Greydawn finally unravels the magic binding Aevin Thornchanter into plant form. The pair then use their combined learning to produce a wine fermented from juiced narinocha pods, that proves highly popular in the courts of Ulthuan.

264 In a last ditch attempt to win the war, the Witch King launches a desperate winter offensive across the Shadowlands. Protected by spells against the cold, his army advances. They take several Elf fortresses and precipitate the most bitter fighting ever seen between the Elves, including the infamous Siege of Tor Lehan. After this battle there were no survivors on either side.

300 Anlec is destroyed. No stone is unscoured. The Altar of Khaine is toppled into the sea.

303 A great armada sails for the Blighted Isle and Naggaroth. The Battle of the Waves is fought on the Blighted Isle. Tethlis dies afterwards under mysterious circumstances. The armada turns back.

Fall of The Slayer
Tethlis died, murdered in cold blood at the Altar of Khaine. Witnesses claim that he was slain by a Dark Elf Assassin, while others speculate that Tethlis's own White Lion bodyguard struck him down for fear that he might draw the Widowmaker.

Bel-Korhadris, The Scholar King
(Imperial Calendar -690 to 498)

The foundations of the White Tower of Hoeth are laid down and the longest period of continual peace in Elf history begins. **11**

The White Tower is completed. The Order of Sword Masters is incepted. **1187**

400 The first Loremasters assemble round the half-complete tower. An entire town of mages and scholars springs up within its shadow.

Aethis, The Poet
(Imperial Calendar 499 to 1120)

Artists, poets and the like begin to congregate in Aethis' court in Saphery. **16**

Murders and abductions in the cities of Ulthuan increase to almost epidemic levels. Aethis, instructs his agents to commence investigations. **182**

Explosive growth of the seaport of Lothern begins. The Cult of Pleasure makes a secretive reappearance. The Sword Masters of Hoeth begin their long secret war against the Cult. **203**

Sword Master Celedrin exposes a Cult of Pleasure in Lothern. Fifteen cultists are killed in the fighting before the remainder surrender. The survivors are put to death. **498**

107 The great statue at Griffon Gate is completed. Its fearsome appearance strikes terror into the hearts of the Elves' enemies, but it is also a memorial to the countless Elf warriors who have died defending it.

200 Representatives of the Phoenix King arrive in Cathay. They return laden with silk, jade and spices. Trade between east and west begins to flourish.

255 Dark Elf slave-ships begin roaming the globe and bring entire tribes to Naggaroth in chains.

621 Aethis is assassinated by his own chancellor, a secret follower of the Cults of Excess.

Morvael, The Impetuous
(Imperial Calendar 1121 to 1502)

The High Elf expedition to Naggaroth is massacred by the Dark Elves, aided by a screaming horde of drugged slave warriors. **2**

The Griffon Gate is besieged. Morvael appoints Mentheus of Caledor as his general and introduces the levy system of mandatory universal military service that will eventually produce the great citizen-soldier armies of Ulthuan. **12**

Mentheus of Caledor
Although history knows him as the Impetuous, Phoenix King Morvael in fact made many shrewd decisions, including electing Mentheus as the general of Ulthuan's armies. Mentheus was a superb military leader and a strong warrior who valiantly led the armies under his control to a number of significant victories. Additionally, Mentheus penned a number of works on the nature of tactics and the art of warfare, several of which have been preserved in the Tower of Hoeth as the finest examples of tactical instruction.

10 The Dark Elves rebuild the citadel of Anlec in the Shadowlands.

20 The siege of Griffon Gate drags on. The great keep is completely encircled by triple rings of ditches and war machines.

25 Siege of Griffon Gate finally lifted by Mentheus leading an army mainly composed of spearmen and archers from Cothique and Chrace.

82 The Fortress of the Dawn is built at the southern tip of the Dark continent.

97 The Citadel of Sunset is built at the southern tip of Lustria.

380 Mentheus is slain assaulting Anlec. His Dragon, Nightfang, goes berserk and routs the Dark Elves. Wracked with grief Morvael re-enters the sacred flame, committing ritual suicide.

Bel-Hathor, The Sage
(Imperial Calendar 1503 to 2162)

200 Norse raids begin. Magnus the Mad arrives to besiege Lothern with 200 men. Confronted by the 10,000 strong Sea Guard of Lothern he orders his men to charge.

400 Facing ever increasing numbers of Norse raids, the Mages of Saphery draw a shroud of mists over the eastern sea approaches to Ulthuan. Bel-Hathor issues his interdict forbidding humans to set foot on Ulthuan.

498 Finubar departs for the Old World, landing at the Bretonnian port of L'Anguille. He travels extensively over the Old World, opening relations with the Empire, Bretonnia and even, tentatively, with the Dwarfs.

530 Finubar reaches Athel Loren and rediscovers the Wood Elves.

548 Finubar returns to Lothern and persuades Bel-Hathor to raise the Interdict. Trade starts to flow into Ulthuan as never before.

Finubar The Seafarer
(Imperial Calendar 2163 to present)

10 N'Kari runs amok across Ulthuan. Loremasters of the White Tower speculate that he is attempting to eliminate the lineage of Aenarion. N'Kari is eventually slain at the Shrine of Asuryan. Survivors of the battle there tell of the bravery of a pair of young Elven twins.

138 The Great Chaos Incursion. Dark Elves invade Ulthuan with many Chaos allies. The Everqueen is saved by Tyrion. Teclis forges his sword and departs the White Tower. The Witch King is defeated at the Battle of Finuval Plain. Teclis leaves with Finreir and Yrtle to join Magnus the Pious in the fight against Chaos in the Old World.

140 The Dark Elves are driven out of Ulthuan after two years of relentless warfare.

141 Teclis founds the Colleges of Magic in Altdorf.

144 The Dark Elf Assassin coterie led by Gloreir attempt to kill the Phoenix King. Finubar is successfully protected by the White Lions, and Korhil and his warriors pursue the Dark Elves throughout Lothern. The remaining assassins are butchered in a swirling battle that rages across the rooftops of the city.

The Imperial Colleges of Magic

One of the greatest altruistic acts of the High Elves was the founding of the Imperial Colleges of Magic by the High Elf Mage Teclis. This single act has done more to protect the Empire, and the other races of Men, against Chaos than almost any other. It has diluted a little of the fear Men hold towards magic, and armed them against the dread power of the Dark Gods. In the years since, the relationship between the Empire and the High Elves has been greatly strengthened by this gesture.

163 Teclis returns to Ulthuan and takes up the position of High Loremaster in the Tower of Hoeth.

221 Caradryan of Eataine is named as the new Captain of the Phoenix Guard, Moraelir the previous Captain willingly standing aside in accordance with Asuryan's Will.

260 Eltharion, son of Moranion, leads a highly successful raid against Naggarond itself. It is the first time High Elves have entered Naggarond and returned alive.

262 Grom the Paunch of Misty Mountain, a notorious Goblin king, sails from the Old World at the head of a mighty Goblin war host. Landing in Yvresse, the horde ravages eastern Ulthuan before being defeated by an Elf army led by Eltharion at Tor Yvresse. Eltharion becomes the Warden of Tor Yvresse.

339 Erik Redaxe raids Cothique at the head of a great fleet of Norse reavers. An Elf war fleet led by Tyrion defeats the Norse in a huge sea battle and drives them away from the coast.

The Waystones of Ulthuan

This image shows a Waystone as found in north eastern Yvresse, after the invasion of Grom the Paunch of Misty Mountain. During his rampage, the Goblin warlord destroyed a number of Waystones, throwing Yvresse into turmoil. Once the Goblin invasion was repelled and peace was restored, the ruined Waystones were repaired or replaced under the guidance of Cyeos, Belannaer and Anurion.

THE FORCES OF ULTHUAN

This section of the book details the forces of a High Elf army. It provides the rules necessary to use all of the elements of the army in your games of Warhammer. Every character and regiment is described, including some of Ulthuan's greatest heroes, such as the noble Prince Tyrion or Eltharion, the Warden of Tor Yvresse. Any special rules that apply to a particular model are given here, including the rules for High Elf Mages and their own Lore of Magic.

Special Rule – Valour of Ages

When the High Elves war with their sundered kin there is not one amongst the host who does not give his all. Uncertainty, dread, dismay; all are banished from the mind until the din of battle fades and weapons can be set at ease once more.

High Elves (not including any mounts) may re-roll any failed psychology tests when fighting a Dark Elf army.

Special Rule – Speed of Asuryan

The High Elves possess a natural skill that far outstrips what ordinary mortals possess. When combined with decades of martial training, it creates a warrior elite the likes of which few can comprehend. Discipline and precision are the hallmarks of the High Elf warhost and every soldier knows his place, and can trust those around him to do likewise.

Each warrior practices his function until he is able to react with lightning speed to any situation. The result of such intense and effective training is an army that can think faster, act more decisively and is more proficient than any other.

All High Elves have the special rule "Always strikes first", regardless of the weapon they are wielding. See the main rule book for details of this special rule.

Note that this special rule applies only to the High Elves, and not to any mounts they are riding or creatures pulling chariots - which will strike in the usual order.

Ulthuan's greatest strength lies in a military both skilled and diverse. If his land is threatened, an Elven lord can count upon aid from all corners of the High Elf kingdoms. First to answer the call are the Archer and Spearman regiments of the lord's own domain and the nobles of his court – these are the bedrock upon which the armies of Ulthuan are built. As word spreads and the true extent of the danger becomes known, phalanxes of Sea Guard answer the call with the uncomplaining determination of true veterans. Hard upon their heels come swift horsemen from Ellyrion and charioteers from Tiranoc, considered brash by the standards of the High Elves, but with valourous hearts all.

Of the many legendary factions the fabled Sword Masters of Hoeth are the swiftest to lend their support to a growing warhost. Dozens of Sword Masters travel Ulthuan, performing the bidding of their Loremasters. When the rallying cry goes out, all nearby Sword Masters able to put aside their current burdens will do so, and forge themselves into a regiment for the duration of the campaign. Should one of the Loremasters of Hoeth choose to lend his mystical might to the cause, the number of Sword Masters in the warhost can rise quite steeply, as such revered mages rarely appear on the field of battle without an escort of the quicksilver warriors.

As for the Phoenix Guard, they take the battlefield in Asuryan's name whenever they are called to do so. However, so few are the Phoenix Guard when compared with other forces, they can rarely be present in the numbers a general might wish for.

As regal bodyguards, the White Lions of Chrace are loathe to leave their assignments for ought but the direst of tragedies – duty to their charge comes before all. If an Elven lord seeks the presence of the White Lions upon the field, he is well advised to request the aid of the one they protect, and thus gain the service of their bodyguard.

Amongst the most prized of potential allies are the Dragon Princes and Dragon Mages of ancient Caledor – nobles, lords and proud warriors every one. The Dragon Princes cannot be counted upon to muster for the mundane drudgeries of sentry and patrol work – such tasks are for the common folk, not the inheritors of Caledor the Great. They live for the glory of besting dread and mighty foes. But if the leader of an assembling host is wise he will peak the Dragon Princes' interest with the promise of a battle worthy of gods, or perhaps confess that a particular foe is beyond his own humble talents. Lured by such glories, the sons of Caledor would gladly ride to a battle on the far side of the world.

Last, and most secretive of all, are the bitter Shadow Warriors of Nagarythe. Marked forever by lives of constant and bitter struggle, they stand apart from High Elf society and never directly respond to a cry for aid. Nevertheless, many a battle has been swung by an unlooked-for volley of black-fletched arrows, or the silent slaughter of an enemy wizard thought safe amongst his own lines. Though they be shunned and distrusted by their own folk, the bleak wardens of Nagarythe know full well where their loyalties lie.

COMMANDERS

The noble families of Ulthuan have led the High Elves through times of peace and conflict for thousands of years. They pride themselves on their deep sense of honour and mastery of the arts of both diplomacy and war, taught to them from a young age. In times of conflict they demonstrate this prowess through their flexibility, perfectly capable of fighting blade to blade in the press of combat, or commanding vast armies from a distance.

Though they are loyal to the Phoenix King even unto death, every member of the High Elf nobility loves intrigue and politics. Unfortunately, this sometimes means that armies are trusted to individuals based on political alignment, rather than their ability to command. Fortunately these instances are rare, for when the safety of his realm is at stake, the Phoenix King will suffer very little such idiocy. There is no shortage of brave and talented commanders among the Asur, and upon these stalwart Elves the Phoenix King can rely.

Most High Elf nobles master the art of warfare as a member of the Silver Helm knights, elite bands of Elven warriors who fight atop majestic Elven steeds. Once they have proven themselves as a Silver Helm, these young nobles are free to perfect other styles of fighting. Depending on their wealth and the kingdom of their birth they fight in many different ways. The Princes of Tiranoc typically do battle from the back of swift and deadly chariots, while the lords of Lothern often stand, spear and bow in hand beside the regiments of Sea Guard. Those with the greatest wealth may ride upon a Great Eagle or Griffon or in the case of the mightiest Princes of Caledor upon a Dragon. Such steeds are invariably a symbol of status, as well as a deadly advantage in battle.

Wherever they hail from, High Elf commanders are agile and incredibly dangerous, able to strike down their foes with a swiftness that few can match. They are experts with a myriad of weapons, equally deadly with a lance, spear, halberd, or longbow, able to penetrate even the most resolute defence with a spear thrust or shoot a foe through the eye while riding at full gallop. The noblest can arm themselves with weapons of legend, magical heirlooms fashioned upon Vaul's forge and held by their families for hundreds if not thousands of years.

The sharp, incisive minds of Ulthuan's nobility make them the finest generals in the world, able to read the ebb and flow of battle before it unfolds. They possess courage that is second to none, and an unshakable sense of duty to both their warriors and their nation. Much is expected of the lords of Ulthuan for they, more so than any others, will shape the future of the High Elves.

	M	WS	BS	S	T	W	I	A	LD
Prince	5	7	6	4	3	3	8	4	10
Noble	5	6	6	4	3	2	7	3	9

Special Rules:
Valour of Ages; Speed of Asuryan (see page 43).

Khaine, the Bloody Handed God
Khaine is the Elf god of war, murder, hatred and destruction. He is the destroying god, who represents to the Elves the fact that in order for there to be life there must also be death, in order to have peace there must also be war, in order to have happiness there must be suffering, in order to have love there must be hatred and murder.

Unlike the Dark Elves, who worship Khaine exclusively, the High Elves balance the destructive nature of Khaine among the other gods, each representing a part of their character. The High Elves see Khaine as the god of unleashed violence. His murder lust is there to be used when danger threatens, but it must be controlled and used wisely. The Nobles of Nagarythe in particular are wary of the lure of Khaine's glories, and know the seductive call of the Bloody Handed God better than any. They live in the twilight of Khaine's immortal shadow, forever reaching towards the light.

MAGES

By the efforts of the High Elf Mages Ulthuan is kept from sinking beneath the waves and the dread powers of Chaos are kept at bay. The need for powerful Mages and careful, scrupulous mastery of magic in High Elf society is as great as anywhere, and the Elves that devote their lives to magic are treated with the same respect and honour as lords.

The High Elves have always been a magical race, and it is common amongst the High Elves to exhibit some talent in the subtle art of sorcery. Saphery is the realm most famed for its mages, and all the princes and nobles of that realm are sorcerors of awesome power. Such is the reputation of that place that Elves from across Ulthuan flock there, to learn the arts of magic from the greatest practitioners in the world.

In the age of the Phoenix King Bel-Korhadris, the White Tower of Hoeth was constructed and it is here that the seat of magical learning upon Ulthuan can now be found. Only those who are most magically gifted, and have proven their dedication beyond doubt, are given the privilege of being taught within the White Tower. There the greatest collection of mages, loremasters and scholars in the world strive to perfect their mastery of the sorcerous arts. It is a place of wonders unbounded, where Mages strive to harness every aspect of the Winds of Magic.

In times of strife, the Phoenix King will beseech the Tower of Hoeth for aid, and the Loremasters of Saphery never shirk from their duty. The Mages who accompany the High Elf armies are truly masters of their art. With skill derived through arduous study they deflect the spells of the enemy, becalming the Winds of Magic themselves, as they put years of learning and lore into practice. A swiftly spoken incantation by a High Elf mage can embolden wavering allies, summoning the glory of the Golden Age of Ulthuan to the minds of the High Elves and steadying fearful hearts. Likewise, a mage can immolate an entire regiment of enemy warriors - directing the vengeful fires of Asuryan against the foe and blasting flesh from bone.

Traditionally High Elf Mages fulfil an advisory capacity when they join the armies of Ulthuan. Wise commanders willingly lean on the advice of a mage that accompanies him, for such is their learning from the arcane tomes contained within the White Tower that Mages possess an insight that is beyond the grasp of those who cannot wield magic. A mage often knows well how to confront the more bizarre foes like the Undead or Daemons of Chaos. They alone can plan for the protection of their fellows against enemy spells. Such versatility has even led to Mages being given command of whole armies, a state of affairs that is especially common for the armies of Saphery.

	M	WS	BS	S	T	W	I	A	LD
Archmage	5	4	4	3	3	3	5	1	9
Mage	5	4	4	3	3	2	5	1	8

Magic:
High Elf Mages and Archmages may choose their spells from High Magic, or any of the Lores of Magic that are presented in the Warhammer rule book.

Special Rules:
Valour of Ages; Speed of Asuryan (see page 43).

Dragon Mages
Among the Mages of Ulthuan, there are a few who spurn their training at the White Tower, leaving the care of their tutors and embarking on a life of violence and warfare within the armies of Ulthuan. These are the Dragon Mages, vibrant and impetuous youths to whom the call to ride to war upon a Dragon is an irresistible urge.

Though few in numbers, the impact of the Dragon Mages upon the armies of Ulthuan has been massive, for they have a natural affinity with the slumbering Sun Dragons, and can awaken them for battle with little more than a spoken word.

THE ARTS OF SAPHERY

In Saphery, at the legendary White Tower, the High Elf Mages strive to perfect the arts of magic. They easily master the coarse magic that lesser races spend a lifetime crudely bending to their will. An aspirant to the White Tower is expected to swiftly gain a proficiency of the eight Lores of Magic, and once they have shown sufficient prowess, their true education can begin. Through decades, often centuries of painstaking research and scrupulous study they begin the long task of learning to master magic in its purest form, an art known simply as High Magic.

Only in the White Tower is High Magic taught, and there the greatest concentration of magic users in the world perfects its use. For those who have mastered it, the ebb and flow of the shifting tides of magic are theirs to command. The Winds of Magic themselves can be becalmed, from a raging tempest to a gentle breeze - denying the enemy their violent spells and thwarting their efforts to muster even the smallest enchantment. Many High Elf Mages prefer to bring the lesser lores to battle in defence of their realm, but the greatest always wield High Magic against Ulthuan's foes. At their command arrows unerringly find their targets and shimmering fields of magical energy ward off the weapons of the enemy. The fire of Asuryan himself can be unleashed on the unworthy foe and their magical weapons are rendered useless by the fury of Vaul's forge. High Magic brings hope to the Asur, and doom to their enemies.

High Elf Magic

High Elf Mages easily master the eight Lores of Magic studied by men before beginning the harder task of learning High Magic. This intense level of learning can provide enormous benefits to Ulthuan's armies, since High Elf Mages can bring spells to the battlefield that are ideally suited to take on any given foe.

Any High Elf Mage or Archmage may choose his spells from one of the eight Lores of Magic described in the Warhammer rule book. Alternatively, you can choose to select his spells from the Lore of High Magic contained here, in which case the Mage or Archmage automatically knows the spell Drain Magic - this is a 'free' spell, so a Level two High Elf Mage, choosing from High Magic would know Drain Magic and two other spells. Roll to determine which other spells your Mages know in the usual manner.

- Whenever an army that includes one or more High Elf Mage or Archmage attempts to dispel a spell, the dispel result is increased by 1.

Note: This bonus is not cumulative for having more than one High Elf Mage, so an army with two High Elf mages will still only get +1 to dispel from this source. However, this bonus may still be combined with magic items as normal.

Drain Magic   Cast on 7+

Manipulating the swirling tides in the Winds of Magic with a skill won through years of practice, the Mage becalms the raging winds, making even the simplest magical task an arduous labour.

Drain Magic lasts until the start of the caster's next Magic phase. The casting values of all spells are raised by 3, whether cast by friend or foe. Further uses of this spell by other wizards are cumulative, so a second casting of Drain Magic in the same Magic phase would raise casting values by 6, and so on.

> ### Blessings of Isha
>
> *Before a promising young mage is taught the dangerous path of the True Mage, he will be shown some simple prayers and enchantments to bring down the blessings of the divine Isha. These are far less dangerous for the caster and can be safely employed by even the most untutored Elven mage.*
>
> *These blessings are of limited use upon the battlefield, intended as they are to ease the burden of daily chores carried out by the aspirant, and allow the tutor-mages to assess the potential of their charges, showing who is most favoured by the gods.*
>
> *It is said that the Elven farmers who live near the White Tower never plough their own fields, as every year there is another crop of novices eager to practice their skills.*

HIGH MAGIC

To randomly generate a spell from the High Magic list, roll a D6 and consult the chart below. If you roll the same spell twice for the same Wizard, roll again. Any Mage can automatically swap one spell for Shield of Saphery if you wish.

D6	Spell	Difficulty
1	Shield of Saphery	5+
2	Curse of Arrow Attraction	6+
3	Courage of Aenarion	8+
4	Fury of Khaine	8+
5	Flames of the Phoenix	11+
6	Vaul's Unmaking	12+

Shield of Saphery — Cast on 5+
As the Mage bends the Winds of Magic to his will, a shroud of glittering magical energy descends upon his allies, protecting them from all harm. Arrows and bolts wash harmlessly past the Elves, while sword blows and spear thrusts become enfeebled, robbed of all strength at the Mage's command.

This may be cast on a friendly unit within 18", even a unit in close combat. If successfully cast, that unit has a 5+ Ward save. Shield of Saphery lasts until the start of the caster's next Magic phase.

Curse of Arrow Attraction — Cast on 6+
As the Mage completes his intonations, the air around the foe shimmers with magical energy as it warps and twists. Bolts and arrows that pass into this roiling field of sorcerous power become blessed and strike the foe with unerring precision.

Cast on an enemy unit within 24" of the caster. Any missile fire directed at the unit in the following Shooting phase may re-roll failed rolls to hit. If the unit is targeted by a template or breath weapon then you may re-roll the dice to see if models which are partially covered are hit. The curse has no effect on close combat.

Courage of Aenarion — Cast on 8+
The High Elf Mage draws on the Winds of Magic and channels its power to embolden the Asur around him. All around the caster, High Elves recall the glory of Aenarion and fight on with courage.

The spell lasts until the start of the caster's next Magic phase. Any friendly unit required to take a Break test within 12" of the caster counts as stubborn.

Fury of Khaine — Cast on 8+
Calling on the dread might of Khaine, the mage launches a searing bolt of brilliant white energy at his enemies.

The Fury of Khaine is a magic missile with a range of 24". It causes 2D6 Strength 4 hits.

Flames of the Phoenix — Cast on 11+
Pure white flames emerge from the air itself and envelop the target immolating the unworthy foe. With every passing second the flames grow hotter, swiftly intensifying until they can sear flesh or even melt steel.

Remains in Play. This may be cast on an enemy unit within 24". Each model, including characters and champions, takes a Strength 3 hit immediately. If the spell is still in play at the start of the caster's next Magic phase, each model in the unit takes a Strength 4 hit. If in play at the start of the caster's following Magic phase, each model takes a Strength 5 hit, and so on, with the Strength increasing by 1 each turn that it remains in play. All wounds inflicted by this spell are flaming attacks.

Vaul's Unmaking — Cast on 12+
Glowing swords grow dim, blood-warm chalices cool and enchanted scrolls crumble into dust, their magical energies drained as the Mage turns the fury of Vaul's forge upon the magical trappings of the enemy.

May be cast on an enemy unit within 24" of the caster and may be cast into close combat. If successfully cast, the owner of the unit must reveal to the caster all the magic items in the unit. The caster then chooses one of them to be nullified. This item loses all of its magical properties.

Items like hand weapons, shields or armour will become 'mundane' items of the same type, while talismans, scrolls and the like will be rendered completely useless.

ARCHERS

The bulk of Ulthuan's armies are composed of Spear and Archer regiments. These expertly trained and finely armed and armoured warriors are actually citizen soldiers of Ulthuan. Every Elf, though he may be craftsman, tradesman or artist in peace time, must become a resolute and deadly fighter in time of war.

Over a thousand years ago, in a time of desperate need, the Phoenix King Morvael introduced a levy system whereby all Elves received military training so that they could be called upon to fight for the defence of their homeland at any time. These levies were organised into companies based within their cities, towns and villages. Morvael accurately predicted the need for a well organised but flexible army to defend Ulthuan in the troubled times that lay ahead. This system has stood the test of time and remains the cornerstone of most Elven armies to this day. It is common for a High Elf to spend twenty or thirty years as part of the same Archer regiment – a short time for those as long lived as the High Elves.

When a High Elf begins his martial training he will first be educated in the rudiments of warfare, armed with a finely wrought sword and a longbow. He is educated in the use of both of these weapons until his skill far exceeds that of a man, and only then is he allowed to see battle as an Archer. In disciplined ranks, these Archer regiments of Ulthuan unleash accurate volleys of arrows upon their foes.

The longbows of the High Elves are constructed from alternating layers of wood, taken from the many forests around Ulthuan, which endow them with great power and range. Each Archer maintains his own weapons, and a great deal of pride and care is placed into the act of fletching new arrows for war. An Archer will often carve intricate patterns or runes onto the shaft of his individual arrows, so that after a battle he can prove which foes were slain by his shots.

The leaders of the High Elf Archer regiments are known as the Hawkeyes, and they are counted among the finest archers in the world. In Elven mythology, hawks are considered the swiftest of the hunters of the skies and the Hawkeyes bear their title with pride. Unlike the other members of Ulthuan's Archer regiments, the Hawkeyes do not move on to join Spear regiments. Having proven their expertise, a Hawkeye's services are retained indefinitely, allowing him to pass his experience on to new citizen warriors.

	M	WS	BS	S	T	W	I	A	LD
Archer	5	4	4	3	3	1	5	1	8
Hawkeye	5	4	5	3	3	1	5	1	8

Special Rules:
Valour of Ages; Speed of Asuryan (see page 43).

Morai-Heg

Morai-heg the Crone is the Elf goddess of the underworld. She is an ancient and withered creature, the Keeper of the Souls and the Weaver of Prophecy. She, and she alone, knows the future and reads the patterns of time from stones carved with runes. She sets the stars of the heavens, and thus the future can be read from the night sky. The High Elves believe that Morai-heg knows the fate of all, and that death is foretold by the Crone herself.

Ravens are said to be Morai-Heg's messengers. They soar across Ulthuan and the barbaric lands of the younger races, bearing snippets of the Crone goddess' wisdom to those that have the wit to interpret the signs. Thus Ulthuan's Archer regiments hark at every coarse ravensong, and mourn the passing of each member of the chorus. Such actions are thought to be the obsessions of simple minds by some of the nobility, but the Archers care not. It does not do to mock the Morai-heg, they say. She knows whether the arrows they loose will find their mark or not, and such knowledge grants a power that should not be offended.

SPEARMEN

Once a High Elf Archer has proven his worth, fighting with his regiment for a decade or more, he is trained to fight as part of a Spear regiment, using the tall spears that the High Elves favour. After only a short time a regiment of High Elf Spears becomes a finely honed fighting machine. Each member of the unit instinctively knows the mind of his comrades to either side and the whole regiment intuitively fights as one body. Each warrior plays his part as if their every movement was part of a carefully choreographed plan, overlapping one another and providing protection, or opening the defenses of the enemy without so much as a spoken word or a nod. Such training serves only to improve upon the natural prowess of the High Elves, and it has earned them a reputation for which they are rightly feared by their foes.

Sentinel is the title given to the Elves who command the Spear regiments, and theirs is the duty to oversee the training of their comrades. Without exception they are veterans of many bloody battles, who have faced countless horrors and lived. Their hard-won experience benefits the Elves around them, instilling confidence as well as providing the regiment with a hardened warrior to take on the worst the enemy has to throw at them.

Like the regiments of Archers, the High Elf Spear regiments are garbed in white, often with a coloured border design that proclaims their realm or city of origin. For the High Elves white is the colour of purity and of death, and their robes symbolise their determination to fight to the end if necessary. Elf Spearmen are very well equipped, with fine hauberks of scale armour, strong shields, tall helms, and spears up to ten feet tall.

On the field of battle, the Spear regiments form bastions of resistance against the enemy. A wall of deadly spear tips threatening to impale any brave enough to charge them. Thanks to their expert training over many years, Elves become so proficient as to completely outstrip the spearmen of other races.

At the Siege of Tor Yvresse, a lone regiment of Spearmen from the Tor Yvresse militia held the narrow procession to the Warden's tower against overwhelming odds. When Eltharion and his warriors finally battled their way through the press to relieve them, they found the last dozen Elf Spearmen grimly standing their ground, amid scores of their fallen comrades and hundreds of slain Goblins.

	M	WS	BS	S	T	W	I	A	LD
Spearman	5	4	4	3	3	1	5	1	8
Sentinel	5	4	4	3	3	1	5	2	8

Special Rules:

Valour of Ages; Speed of Asuryan (see page 43).

Martial Prowess: High Elf citizen soldiers rely heavily on their excellent training and peerless discipline to survive against foes far more brutal and savage. High Elves armed with spears may fight with one extra rank to the front only. This means they normally fight in three ranks, or two in a turn that they charge.

> *Kolgar of the Norse flinched as at an unspoken command the first rank of the Elves lowered their spears and thrust forward. He raised his shield and felt the thump of steel on wood. Instinct saved him, but the distinctive crunch of metal cleaving flesh told him not all of his kinsmen had been so lucky. As the second rank of Elves rammed their spears forward, more Norsemen died. Kolgar stumbled and his helm was pitched from his head as the third rank of Elves stabbed their spears into his men and he heard more screams.*
>
> *Looking into the steely eyes of his foes, Kolgar felt his blood run cold. There was no fear upon the faces of the Elves, only ruthless determination. With a silent prayer to Khorne, Kolgar hoped the Blood God was with him.*

LOTHERN SEA GUARD

Lothern is the greatest city in Ulthuan and capital of Eataine, the most powerful of all the Elven kingdoms. Just as the people of every Elven realm provide Spear and Archer regiments, so the city of Lothern provides the majority of the fighting crews of the Phoenix King's fleet. The Sea Guard can fight as effectively on land as on sea, and are equally resolute defending the walls of Lothern as battling across the decks of Elven warships.

Most Elven soldiery is called to arms only in times of great need, for there are too few Elves to maintain large armies all the time. The Sea Guard, however, is always kept at strength and retains a core of full-time warriors. When the armies of Ulthuan go to war, the Sea Guard go with them, to crew the many warships and secure beachheads enabling the rest of the army to come ashore.

The function of the Sea Guard means that they must fulfil the dangerous tasks of defending their vessels from attack, mounting boarding actions against enemy ships and attacking coastal positions. To achieve this, they are armed with both spears and bows, the better to achieve their many tasks - combining the best aspects of Elf Spearmen and Archers. Those who have witnessed the Lothern Sea Guard in action

can attest to their practiced skill, disembarking effortlessly from their boats as the keel brushes against the shore. Advancing in a disciplined formation through the churning foam, spears lowered and bows at the ready.

Lothern houses the numerous Sea Guard regiments when they are not in active service, and the regiments maintain a number of large and well equipped barracks. These buildings, like any Elven structure, look elegant from the outside, however the eagle-claw bolt throwers mounted in the ornate minarets and upon shimmering blue-tiled roofs bear solemn testament to their martial purpose. Lothern is the one place in Ulthuan where a non-Elf may walk with any degree of freedom and the Sea Guard stoically ensure the protection of Ulthuan's greatest city. Each Sea Guard regiment spends three seasons of the year actively patrolling the seas around their island home and protecting Ulthuan's colonies, and it is in the remaining quarter that they recruit new warriors and hone their skills.

While other seafaring nations, like the Norse, the men of Marienburg and even the Empire, proclaim the excellence of their own ship-borne warriors, there is no doubt that the Sea Guard are the finest marines in the Old World and beyond.

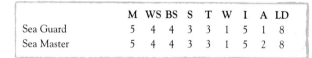

	M	WS	BS	S	T	W	I	A	LD
Sea Guard	5	4	4	3	3	1	5	1	8
Sea Master	5	4	4	3	3	1	5	2	8

Special Rules:
Valour of Ages; Speed of Asuryan (see page 43).

Martial Prowess (see page 49).

Sea Lord Aislinn
The current Sea Lord, Aislinn, is a phenomenal tactician and an implacable foe. Under his control the High Elf fleet has gained scores of impressive victories. While none question his successes, it has been noted that Lord Aislinn carries out his duties with ruthless enthusiasm and an air of viciousness that many in the courts of Ulthuan find distasteful.

Determined to stop Norse raids upon Ulthuan altogether, Aislinn has overseen a violent campaign of attacks on the Norscan coastline. Warriors of the Sea Guard, bolstered by Shadow Warriors have wiped out entire Norse settlements, spreading confusion and fear along the coast. Battle hardened Sea Guard scythe down defenders with volleys of arrows and salvoes of bolts from their Bolt Throwers. Any enemy warriors that manage to survive the onslaught must battle the grim faced Lothern Sea Guard in their serried ranks, spears lowered. Once the defenders have fled, or been slain, the settlement is razed to the ground, and the Sea Guard melt away into the morning mists.

SILVER HELMS

While the common citizens of Ulthuan fill the ranks of
Spearmen and Archers, the Elven nobles satisfy a different
aspect of the High Elf army. For millennia Elven nobles have
learnt to fight from horseback as regiments of knights. These
Elven knights form a small but powerful part of the Phoenix
King's armies, mounted upon swift Elven steeds, armoured in
hardened steel, and bearing tall lances with diamond-hard
tips. The Elven word for knight is Ithiltaen, which literally
means Silver Helm, a title that is derived from their
distinctive headgear. The first Silver Helms rode with the
armies of Aenarion in the great war against the Daemons,
and it is rare now to find an army of the High Elves that does
not include them.

Few Humans can equal the martial prowess of the Silver
Helms, nor their superb horsemanship. Such is the trust that
the Elven steeds have in their masters that they will ride
unflinching into the din of battle, without so much as a
spoken instruction. The bond that joins Silver Helm and
steed requires none of the goading or brutality that lesser
races implement to force their ignoble horses into battle.
For the Silver Helms are true cavalry masters, and their fine
steeds know their commands as if they shared one mind.

It is during their time fighting with the Silver Helms that the
nobles of Ulthuan can truly prove themselves, and it is rare
for an Elven prince or noble to be given command of a force
of any size unless he has proven his valour within the ranks of
the Silver Helm knights first. With this in mind, the warriors
who make up the Silver Helms are often considered reckless,
willing to throw themselves into the most dangerous battles.
They do so in the understanding that glory awaits them
should they prevail, and all are arrogant enough to believe
they can succeed, no matter the odds. At the Battle of
Finuval Plains, the Silver Helms were the first regiment to
reach the stranded Prince Tyrion, racing to his side even as
the treacherous Dark Elves sought to murder him. With
Tyrion at their head they clove through the Dark Elf
formation, trampling scores of Dark Elves beneath their
hooves and driving deep into the Druchii lines.

Silver Helms are proud and defiant warriors, utterly
convinced of their own superiority, and the folly and
ignorance of the soldiers from lesser races.

	M	WS	BS	S	T	W	I	A	LD
Silver Helm	5	4	4	3	3	1	5	1	8
High Helm	5	4	4	3	3	1	5	2	8
Elven Steed	9	3	0	3	3	1	4	1	5

Special Rules:
Valour of Ages; Speed of Asuryan (see page 43).

A ll Silver Helms wear the traditional Ilthilmar helms that
set them apart from other Elven knights. Status in the
Silver Helm regiments is denoted by the decoration and
ornamentation that is added to the helm over the years.
Thus a warrior who has shown particular valour, or bested
a dangerous foe in battle might adorn his helm with silken
ribbons that flow behind him as he rides, while a knight who
has slain a Daemon could have the icon of the burning sun,
set with a single red gemstone on his. There is a decoration for
almost every martial feat imaginable, and veteran Silver
Helms often have incredibly ornate and impressive headgear.

Of all the decorations that the Silver Helms prefer, only those
who have served as the champion of a Silver Helm regiment,
known as the High Helm, may wear the feathers of an Eagle
on his helm. Such embellishment symbolises great skill and is
the mark of a born leader.

Though all Silver Helms vie for the right to wear the Eagle
feathers of the High Helm, it is a role fraught with peril.
A High Helm is expected to fearlessly seek out the champions
and leaders among the enemy and slay them, no matter how
dreadful they may be.

SHADOW WARRIORS

to their long and bitter duty. The hatred that the Shadow Warriors reserve for the Dark Elves knows no bounds, for the Sundering cost them not just their lands and loved ones, but also stained their reputation forever with suspicion and dread. Any Dark Elf captured by the Shadow Warriors can expect a long and painful death.

At some point, every race has felt the wrath of the Shadow Warriors, for they go before the armies of the Asur wherever they fight, slaughtering the enemy's scouts and clearing a path for the main force.

Though they would never speak of it near one of the Nagarythe, the other Elves of Ulthuan perceive an unnerving darkness in the souls of the Shadow Warriors, a taint that hangs over them like a veil of distrust. None question that the Shadow Warriors perform a task necessary for the existence of their homeland, but it has left the Shadow Warriors with stony hearts and a murderous streak to their personalities. Many High Elves have observed the brutal behaviour of their kin from Nagarythe and recoiled in horror. Unsurprisingly, there are High Elves that whisper that the shadow war has left the vicious warriors of Nagarythe more like their Druchii enemies than they would dare to admit.

	M	WS	BS	S	T	W	I	A	LD
Shadow Warrior	5	5	4	3	3	1	5	1	8
Shadow-Walker	5	5	4	3	3	1	5	2	8

Special Rules:
Valour of Ages; Speed of Asuryan (see page 43).

Scout; Skirmish (see rule book for details).

Nagarythe Hatred: Shadow Warriors *hate* all enemies. In addition, when fighting Dark Elves, their *hatred* continues to have an effect in the second and subsequent rounds of combat.

When Nagarythe was riven by civil war, most of the Elves there sided with the Witch King, becoming Dark Elves. Those faithful to the Phoenix King swore to fight Malekith and his treacherous forces. These ill-fated Elves became the Shadow Warriors - the darkest, most sinister and brutal of all the High Elves. From carefully concealed hiding places deep within the Shadowlands these loyal Nagarythe fought a blood-soaked war against Malekith's traitors. In these battles quarter was neither asked nor offered. Generations later the merciless shadow war continues unabated.

The Shadow Warriors are masters of ambush and guerrilla warfare, elite warriors even among other Elves. They strike swiftly and noiselessly from concealment with deadly accurate volleys from their longbows, before charging forth to slay any survivors with a flurry of blades.

Even at times when the populace of Ulthuan does not consider itself at war, there is no respite for the Shadow Warriors. Weary and grim, the Shadow Warriors constantly patrol the barren shores and bleakest hills of Nagarythe. They keep a vigil against approach of the evil Druchii who sank their homeland beneath the waves. To this day Dark Elves return to steal their children and slaughter their kin. It is a lonely and thankless task, to stand as sentinels against the constant malice of the Dark Elves, but the oaths that the Shadow Warriors swore many thousand years ago bind them

Lileath - The Maiden
Lileath is the goddess of the moon, a radiant vision of purity. She is the goddess of dreams and fortune commonly revered by the seers and mages of Ulthuan. Lileath is also the Elven goddess associated with innocence and forgiveness. It is claimed that she reads the intent written upon the heart of an Elf and thus judges his actions, not by what he does but by what he seeks to do.

What is less well known is the special relationship that the Shadow Warriors share with Lileath. She alone is their hope for salvation. If the ill-fated warriors of Nagarythe can finally defeat Malekith's followers and fulfil the oath sworn by their ancestors centuries ago, they believe that the Maiden will forgive them of the grievous wrongs they have committed while carrying out their grisly shadow war.

ELLYRIAN REAVERS

In the time of Caledor, all Ulthuan was in turmoil and the armies of Malekith roamed freely, destroying and slaying at will. The Phoenix King called for brave young horsemen to ride the troubled land. Many answered his call, but the greatest in number by far came from Ellyrion, a land renowned for its fine horses and skilled riders. During the long and bitter war that ended in the Sundering, these valiant riders served Caledor well. In small groups they travelled quickly and secretly across the land, taking messages and soliciting support from amongst the Elven lands, ambushing patrols and intercepting raiders. Caledor named the swift Elven horsemen his Reaver Knights, and they have been known by that title ever since.

These brave horsemen learned to live deep inside enemy territory, finding their sustenance in the wilds and taking what they needed from their foe. They would strike hard and fast before vanishing once more into the wilderness. Soon the evil armies of Malekith became wary of leaving their fortified encampments except in large numbers for fear of attack by the swift knights of Ellyrion. When not fighting they would spread the word of Caledor's struggle, fostering rebellion and helping loyal Elves to escape the clutches of the Witch King.

Stories of their deeds spread amongst Caledor's armies, lending hope to the High Elf cause during the dark days of struggle when all seemed lost. The term Reaver Knight became a byword for dauntless courage and swift skillful warfare. After the war was over and the evil kindred was driven from Ulthuan, Caledor recognised the part played by his Reaver knights and heaped the greatest praise upon these warriors from Ellyrion. He instituted the creation of Reaver bands formed of young Ellryian nobles, which would live in the field for months or even years at a time, watching the coasts for any sign of enemy attack, and patrolling the shoreline of Ulthuan for any sign of Dark Elves or Norse raiders.

To this day the Ellyrian Reavers still form a deadly part of the Phoenix King's armies. Patrolling out of the fortress city of Tor Elyr, the Reaver Knights rove the wild lands of Ellyrion, hunting down and slaying the monstrous beasts that leave the borders of the Annulii and seek to rampage through the Inner Kingdoms. Many a Cockatrice or a Chimera has been laid low by the well-placed arrows or spear thrusts of the noble youths, and many more Dark Elves have had their cruel raids cut short by the swift and deadly Reaver Knights of Ellyrion.

	M	WS	BS	S	T	W	I	A	LD
Ellyrian Reavers	5	4	4	3	3	1	5	1	8
Harbinger	5	4	5	3	3	1	5	1	8
Elven Steed	9	3	0	3	3	1	4	1	5

Special Rules:
Valour of Ages; Speed of Asuryan (see page 43).

Fast Cavalry (see rule book for details).

> We ride until the sun sets and only then do we cease. We look first to our steeds when we halt, for as they care for us when we ride, so we are obliged to care for them as we rest.
>
> Each hoof must be diligently tended, each tired muscle cared for. Of all our weapons, our steeds are the greatest. With them we are swift, tireless, the quicksilver scions of the hunters of old. Without them we would be lumbering and slow, like our foes.
>
> When we strike, it is with bows first and we strike the enemy where he is weakest. Ours is not the way of other knights, we attack swiftly and withdraw before our foes can gather their might. As for nourishment, we take it where we can. When we hunt, we never kill more than is needed, for we need the blessing of Kurnos, and the Hunter god favours not the wasteful nor the cruel...
>
> *Laelinn – Reaver Knight educating aspirants.*

PHOENIX GUARD

Phoenix Guards are the hieratic guardians of the Shrine of Asuryan, the great pyramid temple on an isle in the Sea of Dreams. Inside the shrine it is said there lies the Chamber of Days, and that the histories of Phoenix Kings past, present and future, are written on the ancient walls of the shrine in words of fire upon stone. Any who look upon that wall will know both the future and the past, and will forever be cursed with knowledge of their own death.

The Phoenix Guards do not utter a word, for it is forbidden for anyone who has seen the secrets of time to speak of them, and all who do so take a magical vow of silence from which they can never be released. Viewed by many as a curse, this magical covenant with Asuryan offers them a measure of protection from their foes, and fills them with a sense of purpose bordering on the divine.

When their Lord orders them to war, the Phoenix Guard are grim and resolute, clad in ornate armour, and armed with tall ceremonial halberds. While their stony quiet is unnerving to foes, the aura of fear that surrounds them is far more horrifying. Their eyes blaze with a fiery intensity borne of unshakeable faith in the Creator god of the Elves, and the air around a regiment of Phoenix Guard literally throbs with the raw power of Asuryan. Any who would stand in their way are assailed by an overwhelming sense of dread. On the battlefield Phoenix Guard are always found where the fighting is at the most fierce for they know their destiny – whether they shall live, or the exact moment and manner of their death – and so battle holds no fear for them.

The most famous duty of the Phoenix Guard comes about when a new Phoenix King is elected. It is the role of the Phoenix Guard to accompany the newly chosen Phoenix candidate, and attend him as he enters the flame eternal, which marks his rebirth as the Phoenix King. When a Phoenix King dies, the Phoenix Guard appear without warning, and carry the Phoenix King's body to the White Ship that will convey the King to his final resting place.

From ancient times, before Aenarion and the war against the Daemons, the legions of the Phoenix Guard always numbered ten thousand, and even now their number is the same. This has given rise to legends that the Phoenix Guard are immortal, or at least able to return from the dead. On this subject, like all others, the Phoenix Guard remain silent.

	M	WS	BS	S	T	W	I	A	LD
Phoenix Guard	5	5	4	3	3	1	6	1	9
Keeper of the Flame	5	5	4	3	3	1	6	2	9

Special Rules:
Valour of Ages; Speed of Asuryan (see page 43).

Cause Fear; 4+ Ward Save (see main rule book for details).

> "*Until one has witnessed the Phoenix Guard upon the field of battle, one cannot comprehend the power that they possess. Ranks of highly trained warriors all utterly silent. Around them the very air shimmers, They are not just the guardians of a temple, they are the chosen warriors of a mighty Elven god.*
>
> *No spoken word commands them, yet each knows his place within the battle plan. They do not baulk before even the vilest horrors of the world. It is said that each knows the moment he will die, and I believe it, for they face the maelstrom of battle with unflinching resolve. Who but one utterly convinced of his survival, or demise, could face a hail of arrows, or a charge from some unspeakable monster without flinching?*
>
> *The horrors and the wonders they must have seen, these Phoenix Guard. How I wish they would only speak of it to mortals not gifted with such foresight.*"
>
> Taken from: A Man Among the Elves, by Herwig Algnar.

SWORD MASTERS OF HOETH

The Sword Masters are exemplars of the martial arts, capable of incredible feats of arms. At the White Tower of Hoeth, the greatest seat of learning in the world, these warrior-scholars train arduously, honing their exceptional agility, mastering every nuance and facet of sword fighting. Each Sword Master has studied warfare and personal combat for decades, often centuries - developing an expertise so incredibly complete that there is no group of warriors that can match them.

Sword Masters wield the greatswords of Hoeth. These mighty weapons are elegantly shaped swords, often as long as six or seven feet from the pommel to the tip of the razor sharp blade. A Sword Master wields his weapon with such speed and precision it is said he can raise his sword, sever an enemy's neck and return his sword to rest before a lesser warrior can even raise a shield to block him. Despite being clad in the traditional armour and tall helm of their order, the Sword Masters are more nimble and graceful than any non-Elf could hope to be.

In battle, the Sword Masters are deadly opponents, eager to practice their great skills on the enemies of Ulthuan. Only at war against the foes of the Asur can the Sword Masters truly

unleash all of their ability, testing their learning in an arena where there is no room for mistakes. They fight with great sweeps of their blades, the air itself humming as the Sword Master weaves a web of death that only the very best fighters in the world could hope to survive.

Since their inception during the reign of Bel-Korhadris, the Sword Masters have distinguished themselves on thousands of occasions. At the Battle of Hathar Ford, a single regiment of Sword Masters guarded the only river crossing for miles around. Commanded by the feared sorcerers, the Coven of Ten, a vast Dark Elf army sought swift passage across the river, but the Sword Masters denied them at every turn. Fighting knee-deep in the swirling river, the Sword Masters inflicted grievous casualties on the Dark Elves, despite the blistering barrage of spells cast by the Coven. After hours of ceaseless combat, the river became so choked with the bodies of the Dark Elf dead, that the corpses blocked the flow of the river, which soon burst its banks. The timely arrival of the legendary High Elf Mage Teclis to the battlefield brought much needed respite from the magical assault launched by the Coven of Ten, and the Sword Masters swiftly counter attacked, driving the Dark Elves from the field.

	M	WS	BS	S	T	W	I	A	LD
Sword Master	5	6	4	3	3	1	5	2	8
Bladelord	5	6	4	3	3	1	5	3	8

Special Rules:
Valour of Ages; Speed of Asuryan (see page 43).

The Secret War
Since the time of Bel Shanaar a long and bitter struggle has raged behind the peaceful facade of Ulthuan's courts and palaces. A war fought behind closed doors by the trusted agents of the Phoenix King and the debased worshippers of the Cults of Excess.

After centuries of bitter struggle, Phoenix King Aethis requested aid from the sages of the White Tower. In response the Loremasters of Hoeth unleashed the Sword Masters upon the vile cultists. The legendary warrior-scholars wasted no time taking their unparalleled skills to the dark corners of Ulthuan's great cities, slaughtering the cultists wherever they were found.

So began the first chapter in the secret war that has lasted ever since, for the Sword Masters are implacable foes and will not rest until every member of the Cult of Pleasure lies dead.

TIRANOC CHARIOTS

steeds biting and kicking, even as the riders thrust out with razor-sharp spears. When the chariots of Tiranoc launch a mass charge, the ground trembles beneath the thundering hooves of the Elven Steeds, bringing dread to the enemies of the High Elves.

Many great and noble Elven heroes have hailed from the realm of Tiranoc, and their determination bears witness to the finer qualities of Tiranoc. Bel Shanaar, the second Phoenix King, was a prince of Tiranoc prior to his election, a skilled warrior who had distinguished himself in the wars against the Daemons. Upon his chariot, named Silver Wind, he and his chosen charioteers drove entire Daemon hosts before them. To the Elves who saw them fight, they became known as the Wind Riders. To this day whenever a large force of Tiranoc charioteers is gathered they are referred to as the Riders of the Wind, a mark of respect for the ancient warrior who oversaw the recovery of the High Elf race, and lost his life to the betrayal of Malekith.

	M	WS	BS	S	T	W	I	A	LD
Tiranoc Chariot	-	-	-	5	4	4	-	-	-
Crew	-	4	4	3	-	-	5	1	8
Elven Steed	9	3	-	3	-	-	4	1	-

Special Rules:

Valour of Ages; Speed of Asuryan (see page 43).

Chariot (see rule book for details).

The High Elves of Tiranoc are an adventurous people, proud of their fighting traditions, and deeply embittered by the wars that have ravaged their realm. For the nobles of that land there was no finer thing than to race across the smooth, fertile plains of Tiranoc atop a swift Elven chariot. Like their kin in the Shadow Realm of Nagarythe, the Elves of Tiranoc had most of their land engulfed by the raging seas and many of their grandest mansions and noblest families were lost. Entire cities were swept away by the murderous tidal wave and the once sweeping plains were left sodden marshes. The effort of thousands of years has restored some of Tiranoc's greatness and to this day Tiranoc nobles continue to fight from swift war chariots, just as their forefathers did in the days of Aenarion.

When Dark Elf armies thrust southwards through Tiranoc they are harried at every turn by charioteers and denied the chance to forage and gather supplies. Many a Dark Elf raiding force has been hounded into extinction by the brave warriors and massed chariot charges of Tiranoc.

When the Phoenix King calls his subjects to war, the fiery Nobles of Tiranoc are always among the first to answer. They fight with incredible skill, complementing the awesome speed of the Elven steeds that pull them, darting in between enemy units and raining arrows onto their enemies. When they charge, they crash fearlessly into the ranks of their foes, the

With the thunder of hooves and the turning of our steel-shod wheels, we are death upon the wind.

With bow in hand, ours is a vengeance rained down from afar, we are death upon the wind.

With tall spears held to our foe's throat, cold fury guiding our aim, we are death upon the wind.

From the battle hymn of Tiranoc.

DRAGON PRINCES OF CALEDOR

Caledor is the fabled land of Dragons, where in ancient times princes of royal blood would ride Dragons to battle. The Dragon Princes, as they were called, were the greatest warriors in all of Ulthuan, champions of the wars against the Daemons and the civil war wrought by the Witch King.

Once, Caledor was the supreme realm amongst the Elven kingdoms, but now its power has waned, its Dragons are diminished in size and number, and they spend long centuries in a deep sleep from which they can seldom be roused. Today there are still Dragons slumbering in their lairs in the Dragon Spine Mountains and the caves beneath Vaul's Anvil.

Where in the distant past the nobles of Caledor rode Dragons, today they ride to war as knights upon swift Elven steeds in much the same way as Elves of other lands. However, their old pre-eminence remains a source of pride, their martial traditions are strong, and they regard themselves as the elite even amongst the nobility of Ulthuan's kingdoms. Indeed, 'Prince of Caledor' is a byword for arrogance amongst Elves of other lands.

The ancient traditions are reflected in the Ithilmar armour worn by the Knights of Caledor and their steeds, modelled in the antique style of that worn by Dragon riders of old. In both cases the ornately detailed armour is forged in the heart of a volcano in the Dragon Spine Mountains using ancient enchantments that were perfected when Ulthuan was young. This dragon armour is entirely resistant to heat, in the manner of Aenarion's armour of old. A Dragon Prince clad in his dragon armour can ride fearlessly through fire, be it the breath of dragons, the alchemical fury of the Dwarfs or the eldritch flames of the vile Skaven.

In battle the Princes of Caledor stand aloof from other High Elf regiments. They choose for themselves the most dangerous battlefield assignments, seeking both glory and an opponent worthy of their skills. The finest cavalry in Ulthuan, and some say the world, the Dragon Princes crash into the enemy with arrogant disdain, slaughtering the foe with masterful strikes from both lance and sword. Such is their skill that a Dragon Prince can slay two warriors with one lance thrust, impaling both on their steel-tipped weapon.

	M	WS	BS	S	T	W	I	A	LD
Dragon Prince	5	5	4	3	3	1	6	2	9
Drakemaster	5	5	4	3	3	1	6	3	9
Elven Steed	9	3	0	3	3	1	4	1	5

Special Rules:
Valour of Ages; Speed of Asuryan (see page 43).

Dragon Armour: Forged in the heart of a volcano, this fine armour is enchanted to ward off the effects of Dragon breath. Dragon armour is heavy armour, giving a 5+ armour save. In addition, the model and its mount are immune to all breath attacks, and all Flaming Attacks.

Caledor's Pride
Such is the arrogance of the Dragon Princes that their standards remain erect whilst all the others are dipped to acknowledge the rule of the Phoenix King prior to battle.

When forced to remark upon it, Dragon Princes claim that this stems from the reign of Caledor the Conqueror, who granted them this as a sign of respect for their noble sacrifice. They say that it is not for them to countermand the word of Caledor. Such an act would be to offer far greater disrespect to the lineage of Phoenix Kings than ten thousand erect banners could ever achieve.

Others point out that even before Caledor granted this boon, the Dragon Princes refused to lower their banners anyway.

WHITE LIONS

The White Lions are the personal guard of the Phoenix King. They form a number of substantial regiments that protect the King's palace in peacetime and accompany him in time of war. Traditionally the White Lions are recruited from the rugged land of Chrace, a perilous realm whose inhabitants are great woodsmen and fierce warriors. Those woodsman of Chrace who prove themselves worthy to become a member of the King's elite bodyguard are expert warriors, who fight with long-handled axes. Shoulder to shoulder with their comrades, White Lions are capable of weathering the deadliest assaults before retaliating with swift, crushing blows.

The White Lions trace their origins back to the time of Caledor the First. Caledor was hunting in Chrace when he received the news that he was to be the next Phoenix King. He immediately took the road to the Shrine of Asuryan. On route he was intercepted by Dark Elf assassins who had doubtlessly learned of the new Phoenix King's identity from their spies at court. Caledor would surely have died were it not for the intervention of a party of Chracian hunters who swept out of the forest, throwing the Dark Elves into disarray with the suddenness of their attack, before cutting the assassins down with their axes.

Having overcome the assassins, the Chracians proceeded to escort the Phoenix King to the Shrine, easily avoiding further Dark Elves by means of their expert woodcraft. Caledor adopted the Chracians as his bodyguard, and formed them into a proper regiment based in Lothern.

It is a great honour amongst the Chracians to accompany the Phoenix King, and one which must be earned by slaying a white lion, one of the most dangerous creatures of that wild land. This exceptionally difficult task is the traditional rite of the Chracian warrior, entitling him to wear the lion's pelt as a mark of courage. The pelt has another use too, for the fur of a white lion is abnormally thick, and worn over armour it offers excellent protection against the arrows and shot of their enemies.

White Lion regiments are often despatched to join the armies of Ulthuan during times of particular danger, tasked with protecting High Elf generals, mages or bolstering the overall strength of the army. White Lions are renowned for their unflinching courage in the face of overwhelming odds and terrible horrors, protecting their charge whatever the foe and regardless of the danger to themselves.

	M	WS	BS	S	T	W	I	A	LD
White Lion	5	5	4	4	3	1	5	1	8
Guardian	5	5	4	4	3	1	5	2	8

Special Rules:

Valour of Ages; Speed of Asuryan (see page 43).

Stubborn (see rule book for details).

Woodsmen: The hunters of Chrace are woodsmen beyond compare, able to navigate forests with ease. White Lions and any characters that are joined to their unit may move through woods without penalty.

Lion Cloak: Each White Lion wears the fur of a slain lion, both as a sign of status and a protection against harm. White Lions add +2 to their armour save against shooting attacks.

The Woodman's Axe

Although every Phoenix King since Caledor the Conqueror has offered his bodyguard their choice of replacement weaponry, White Lion's continue to proudly bear the traditional woodman's axe into battle. Many of the axes carried by the White Lion's are ancient heirlooms, handed down from father to son and warrior to warrior across centuries untold, yet their steel remains untarnished and never loses its keen edge. When wielded by the immensely strong Chracian hunters, these weapons are said to be able to fell a tree, or cleave a man in half with but a single blow.

LION CHARIOTS OF CHRACE

Of the wild beasts that prowl within the realm of Chrace, the white lions from which the famed Chracian regiments take their name are the best known. These lions are deadly hunting cats that stand as tall at the shoulder as a horse. Each white lion is capable of rending a foe limb from limb and a swipe of their claws is enough to break a man's neck.

There are accounts of prides of white lions ravaging convoys travelling through the region and even attacking isolated villages should they become hungry enough. A great many songs, poems and tales within Chrace warn of straying too close to a white lion.

It is because of the incredible danger that the white lions present that the Chracian hunters are forced to hunt them with axe, spear and bow through the perilous forests of their homeland. Such encounters between the Elven hunters and white lions all too often go against the High Elves, for such is the sheer savagery of the lions that only the very greatest hunters can expect to triumph.

Not all white lions discovered by Chracian Hunters are killed out of hand, however, for often lion cubs or adolescents are discovered and the High Elves take no joy in needless slaughter. These cubs would doubtless become savage and deadly beasts if they were left in the wild, but with expert care the young white lions are raised to become as loyal as a Griffon. Reared with a tenderness normally reserved for Elven steeds or other noble creatures, these 'tame' white lions swiftly form a bond with the Chracian hunters that foster them. Thereafter these cubs are known as War Lions, for they make formidable weapons upon the battlefield.

When the regiments of Chrace go to war they are often accompanied by powerful War Lions, that draw the famed Lion Chariots. Sturdy war engines made in the traditions of the legendary chariots of Tiranoc, the Lion Chariots are fashioned from the same smooth white wood. These chariots are the finest expression of the Elven artisan's craft. Unlike the swift and nimble Tiranoc Chariots though, the Chariots of Chrace are drawn by a pair of ferocious War Lions, proud beasts whose feline grace and elegantly plaited manes belie their awesome power.

In contrast to the Tiranoc war chariots that sweep across the battlefield carefully picking at the foe, the Lion Chariot of Chrace is a brutal weapon of destruction. Proceeded by savage roars that shake the enemy to their very core, the Lion Chariots plough through skirmishers and crash fearlessly into the ranks of enemy regiments. The paired War Lions tear into the foe with fang and claw, bearing mounted warriors to the ground and creating pandemonium within tightly packed infantry formations. The crew fight from the chariot platform supporting the raging lions with deft blows from their axes, cleaving heads and shoulders with every strike. Such daring charges have become the hallmark of the Lion Chariots, earning them a reputation as courageous linebreakers capable of smashing even the most determined shieldwall.

	M	WS	BS	S	T	W	I	A	LD
Lion Chariot	-	-	-	5	4	4	-	-	-
Crew	-	5	4	4	-	-	5	1	8
War Lions	8	5	-	5	-	-	4	2	-

Special Rules:

Valour of Ages; Speed of Asuryan (see page 43).

Chariot; Cause Fear (see rule book for details).

Kurnus the Hunter

Kurnus the Hunter is the lord of both forest and beasts. He is the husband of Isha, and all Elves are his children. Wherever he travels, Kurnus is followed by a pack of baying hounds and when he sounds his horn the Wild Hunt follows him. Kurnus is the spirit of the untouched forests, wild animals and trackless wilderness.

All hunters venerate Kurnus, for he watches over them in the wilds. He requires that a hunter never kills animals for sport, only slaying wild and dangerous beasts, and only hunting enough game to eat. To offend Kurnus is to invite disaster, for his vengeance is swift and brutal.

REPEATER BOLT THROWERS

The Elves of Ulthuan have never developed the unreliable gunpowder technology favoured by the Men and Dwarfs of the Old World. Indeed they have never needed to, for their marksmanship is such that to rely on such crude weapons could only prove detrimental to their awesome prowess with missile-fire. Instead the Asur rely on the tried and tested war machines that have served their race since the ancient war against the Daemons, the same weapons that saw them through the Sundering and the War of the Beard - the Eagle Claw Bolt Thrower.

The Eagle Claw, or Repeater Bolt Thrower as it is often known, is operated by a torsion and counter-weight system, the result of which is a long, spear-like bolt hurled at the enemy with incredible force and accuracy. Made from composite layers of star wood, which are magically bound together, the Eagle Claw has a strength and accuracy unmatched by the barbarous weapons of other races. Such is the precision that the bolts are thrown with, that an individual warrior can be accurately impaled several hundred yards away. The force of this individual bolt is such that even the mightiest creatures can be severely wounded, if not killed and several men standing in file can easily be skewered by the same shot. The sides of High Elf warships and the battlements of High Elf fortresses bristle with Eagle Claws, manned by constantly vigilant Lothern Sea Guard.

The same Lothern Sea Guard crew the Repeater Bolt Throwers that the High Elves deploy on the battlefield. In such situations, these deadly war machines are turned against massed infantry formations, often firing smaller bolts in rapid succession, hence the term repeater. Loaded in clutches of six, these bolts are each the length of an Elven sword and are launched with enough force to cut down even the best-armoured warriors. Eagle Claw crews are swift and skilled, reloading the bolt thrower fast enough that only seconds separate one deadly volley from another. Any who fight the armies of the High Elves learn quickly to fear the dark clouds of bolts falling like a deadly rain from the heavens.

Repeater Bolt Throwers may lack the outright destructive potential of cannons and the devastating pyrotechnics of mortars, but their elegant potency more than compensates. The ability to accurately fire bolt after bolt, without fear of malfunction, makes them amongst the most dreaded war machines in the world.

	M	WS	BS	S	T	W	I	A	LD
Bolt Thrower	-	-	-	-	7	3	-	-	-
High Elf Crew	5	4	4	3	3	1	5	1	8

Special Rules:

Valour of Ages; Speed of Asuryan (see page 43).

Volley: Repeater Bolt Throwers can fire in one of two ways. Each Shooting phase, the Repeater Bolt Thrower may either shoot a single bolt (see the rule book under Bolt Throwers) or may fire a volley.

If using the volley option then the Repeater Bolt Thrower shoots six bolts in the Shooting phase. These shots cannot pierce ranks and only inflict one wound each, rather than D3. All bolts must be directed against a single target. Volleys have a range of 48", Strength of 4, with armour saves suffering a -2 penalty.

Note: The Repeater Bolt Thrower is incredibly accurate and is not subject to the Multiple Shots special weapon rule.

> "*An army that seeks to fight without the protection of the Eagle Claws is clearly courageous or inept. Either way, I wish no part in it.*"
>
> Eolaran Greyhawk, Seamaster.

GRIFFONS

Griffons are huge beasts that appear to be formed from a curious mixture of creatures. They have large heads and a razor-sharp beak like a bird of prey, with forelegs and wings to match. Their hindquarters however, are like those of a great hunting cat, complete with clawed rear legs and a long tail. A Griffon will typically grow to be two or three times the size of a horse and is easily strong enough to bear an Elf aloft and into battle upon its back.

The Griffons that live high in the Annulii, or upon the rocky slopes of Chrace are dangerous and wild. For an Elf to have a hope of mastering a Griffon, it must be captured and trained while still young. The destructive power of such a creature makes the danger of raising one more than worth the effort, for once trained, Griffons are fiercely loyal, compensating for their deficit in intelligence with a cunning and savagery that makes them the favoured mount of many Elven Lords.

	M	WS	BS	S	T	W	I	A	LD
Griffon	6	5	0	5	5	4	5	4	7

Special Rules:
Fly; Large Target; Terror (see Main rule book for details).

GREAT EAGLES

The pact that binds the Great Eagles to the High Elves is ancient, lasting since the time that the legendary Caradinor and Sulinash rode to war against the Daemons of Chaos.

Compared to Griffons, or even Elven steeds, Great Eagles are highly intelligent and require no training and very little coaxing to join the Elves in battle. Their depth of understanding and their intellect is greater than any creature save perhaps Dragons, and the wisest of the Asur are able to converse with them as if passing the time of day. Great Eagles are haughty and proud creatures though, and they do not suffer foolish company gladly.

When the forces of Chaos or Dark Elves come to raid Ulthuan it is often the Great Eagles who warn of the arrival of the black sailed vessels, and when the High Elves assemble for battle, the noble Eagles join the throng. With powerful talons the Great Eagles swoop down upon the crew of enemy war machines and tear them apart, before using mighty wings to bear themselves swiftly away and out of reach.

	M	WS	BS	S	T	W	I	A	LD
Great Eagle	2	5	0	4	4	3	4	2	8

Special Rules:
Fly (see Main rule book for details).

DRAGONS

A Dragon's massive scaly body is powerfully built and strong enough to shatter city gates. Dragons have great fanged mouths from which they can breathe scorching gouts of flame over their enemies, and taloned claws sharp enough to slice through stone. A Dragon's wings are immense, able to bear it effortlessly through the sky. They are wise and aloof, viewing the world around them with a perspective that only the eldest creatures can share.

On Ulthuan, Dragons are the subject of legends quite different to the terrifying folk tales of the Old World. Without the Dragons of Ulthuan, the High Elves would have been annihilated thousands of years ago. The Dragons are the oldest and greatest allies of the Elves, and the fates of both races are forever intertwined. Within Ulthuan, the realm of Caledor is the home of the Dragons and in ancient days those noble beasts could always be seen riding the thermals of the mountain ranges there. But times have changed. Now, in colossal caverns found deep within the Dragonspine Mountains, the Dragons sleep away the centuries. A mysterious languor that began in the earliest years of Tethlis's reign has caused more and more Dragons to enter a slumber from which only the mages and princes of Caledor can wake them. To ride into battle upon the back of a mighty dragon is

an ancient tradition in the realm of Caledor that sings in the blood of the Elves. It has been known for a prince to spend months if not years giving voice to the ancient songs of awakening, pleading with the slumbering form of an ancient Dragon to rouse and aid the Elves of Ulthuan.

Those seeking to learn the secrets of waking a Dragon are bound by powerful spells cast by Caledorian mages, and it is believed that should they ever seek to divulge their knowledge, they will die. Such a veil of secrecy is essential for the survival of Ulthuan's Dragons. The Dark Elves both covet and hate the Dragons who fight beside the High Elves in equal measure, and Malekith's followers would willingly butcher every one of Ulthuan's Dragons just to deny them to their cousins. In the past, raids have been launched against Caledor by Dark Elf Shades, with the intention of stealing unhatched eggs for their depraved masters. Thankfully such attacks are rare and successes are rarer still. The Dark Elves have some few Dragons of their own, but they are black-hearted monsters twisted by hate and tortured beyond reason, a poor comparison to the noble beasts of Caledor.

Few young Dragons are hatched now on Ulthuan. The youngest Dragons are referred to by the Elves as Sun Dragons, in reference to their hot tempers and the rich, warm hue of their scales. Those Dragons that surpass the Sun Dragons in might and enlightenment are honoured by the Elves with the title of Moon Dragons. Moon Dragons lived before Aenarion and fought in the wars against the Daemons. The oldest and most powerful of Ulthuan's Dragons are referred to as Star Dragons, for they are truly as ancient as the very stars of the firmament. While any Dragon can savage an entire regiment of warriors, tear a manticore apart or rip the head off of a wyvern, a Star Dragon is so physically powerful that it can battle against even the Greater Daemons of Chaos and prevail.

	M	WS	BS	S	T	W	I	A	LD
Sun Dragon	6	5	0	5	6	5	4	4	7
Moon Dragon	6	6	0	6	6	6	3	5	8
Star Dragon	6	7	0	7	6	7	2	6	9

Special Rules:

Fly; Large Target; Terror; Scaly Skin: The older a Dragon grows, the tougher its hide becomes. Sun Dragons have a Scaly Skin save of 5+, Moon Dragons 4+ and Star Dragons 3+ (see Main rule book for details).

Dragon Fire: Each Dragon has a breath weapon. The hits from Dragon Fire are flaming attacks. In addition, any unit that suffers at least one casualty from Dragon Fire must take a Panic test at the end of the phase, exactly as if it had suffered 25% casualties from shooting. The greater the Dragon, the more powerful its Dragon Fire. A Sun Dragon breathes fire with a Strength of 2, a Moon Dragon with Strength 3 and a Star Dragon with a Strength of 4.

DRAGON MAGES

The first known Dragon Mage was Caelith Fireheart. Born in the last year of Aethis the Poet's reign, Caelith was little more than a child in the eyes of the High Elves when he claimed one of the famed Sunstaffs from the Caves of Dreaming and awoke the Sun Dragon Rilgaur. Caelith and the newly awoken Rilgaur brought aid to the army of Mentheus at Griffon Gate, leading a devastating charge that crushed the flank of the Dark Elf host and allowed the wily old Mentheus to rout the enemy from the field. When the fighting was over, Mentheus greeted Caelith and first coined the name Dragon Mage in reference to the courageous young Mage.

In every generation since, a handful of Dragon Mages have emerged from the aspirant Mages studying the Winds of Magic at the Tower of Hoeth. They are found among the most impetuous and fiery students, and almost without exception they are of Caledorian descent. Once they begin to study the Lore of Fire, the first of the Lores taught at the Tower, their aggressive and warlike nature becomes even more apparent. Each is plagued by dreams of fire and blood, in which they ride upon Dragons the colour of the setting sun. Soon the only desire of these youths is to seek out their destiny as a Dragon Mage. Indeed, once they have been approved as competent with Fire magic by their tutors at the Tower, they set off on the long journey back to Caledor and the caves below the Dragon Spine Mountains.

To awaken a Dragon from slumber is a process that can take months, or even years, and yet these impetuous Mages from Caledor take to the task as if born to it. No sooner does a Dragon Mage enter the sulphur-clogged caverns below the Dragon Spine than the dormant Sun Dragons grow restive. Instinctively, and with no instruction, the Dragon Mage will approach one of the sleeping beasts and call it by name - awakening the Sun Dragon fully. Only a Sun Dragon will hear the call of a Dragon Mage and rise for battle – the older and wiser Dragons of the Moon and Stars are not given to such passion and recklessness, awaiting a steadier mind to rouse them.

The Dragon Mages of Caledor have earned themselves a reputation as wild and uncontrolled, qualities that are not normally seen favourably by the High Elves. Yet despite this, the Elves of Ulthuan look upon these fiery youths and the ease with which they bring the Dragons to war, and in them see hope reborn.

	M	WS	BS	S	T	W	I	A	LD
Dragon Mage	5	4	4	3	3	2	6	2	8

Magic:
Dragon Mages use spells from the Lore of Fire.

Special Rules:
Valour of Ages; Speed of Asuryan (see page 43).

Reckless: Dragon Mages are renowned for the fearless manner with which they wield Fire magic, and the lack of heed they pay during their training in Saphery. They summon power with incredible innate talent, but their reckless attitude can often lead to mistakes. When a Dragon Mage casts a spell, a 'free' Power dice is added to the casting attempt. This extra dice can cause a Irresistible Force or a Miscast as normal, and can cause the Dragon Mage to roll more dice than he is normally allowed to. In addition, Dragon Mages do not provide the +1 bonus to Dispel attempts like other High Elf Mages.

Warrior Mage: Warlike and aggressive, Dragon Mages revel in the press of battle, often imbuing their Sunstaff with the deadly magic of Rhuin. When selecting spells prior to the battle, Dragon Mages may choose to swap one of the spells rolled for Flaming Sword of Rhuin, rather than with Fireball as normal.

TYRION
THE DEFENDER OF ULTHUAN

Prince Tyrion is the greatest living warrior of the High Elves. He is a descendant of the first Phoenix King and traces his line from Aenarion's firstborn son, Morelion. He is so valiant and skilled that some Elven bards say that he is Aenarion reborn. Since his meteoric rise to fame during the Great Chaos Incursion, many have spoken in hushed tones of his destiny to lead the High Elves towards a new and glorious future, and perhaps one day to take the Phoenix Crown. If Tyrion hears such gossip, he pays it no heed, for his only concern is the safety and protection of Ulthuan and the Everqueen. He is unswervingly loyal to the current Phoenix King, Finubar the Seafarer.

Tyrion was the first commander at the glorious Battle of Finuval Plain, when he routed the host of the Witch King and slew the Witch King's personal champion, Urian Poisonblade. In that one battle, he made a name for himself that will echo through the ages, and were that his only act his name would be recorded in the Book of Days with honour. His accolades reach further though, for without his quick thinking and the might of his sword arm, the Everqueen herself would have been slain, and all of Ulthuan would have been thrown into turmoil.

Alone among all the courtiers of Avelorn, Tyrion was able to defend the spiritual leader of the High Elves, and whisk her away to safety. It is common knowledge now that Tyrion is the consort to Alarielle herself, and few are surprised. Time and again he has shown the strength of character and the implacable will that made his forefathers great.

In the years since the Great Incursion, Tyrion has busied himself strengthening Ulthuan's armies and all know that whenever danger comes to the High Elves island home, the enemy will be met by Tyrion. He is the protector of the Everqueen and the defender of all Ulthuan.

Tyrion is the greatest living warrior of the High Elves, and arguably the finest soldier in the world today. The combination of potent magic items and heroic ability makes Tyrion the perfect leader for any High Elf army. Enemies of Ulthuan beware!

	M	WS	BS	S	T	W	I	A	LD
Tyrion	5	9	7	4	3	4	10	4	10
Malhandir	10	4	0	4	3	1	5	2	7

Armour:
Dragon Armour of Aenarion.

Weapons:
Sunfang.

Mount:
Tyrion rides the mighty Elven steed Malhandir.

Special Rules:
Valour of Ages; Speed of Asuryan (see page 43).

The Defender of Ulthuan: Prince Tyrion is renowned across the island continent of Ulthuan as the finest warrior of the Elven race. Even Finubar, the Phoenix King bows to Tyrion's incredible wisdom in matters of warfare. If Tyrion is included in your army he is always the General.

Malhandir: Malhandir is literally a creature of legend, the greatest living Elven steed. Malhandir increases Tyrion's Unit Strength to 2. The barding Malhandir wears does not affect his Movement value in any way. Note also, the barding on Malhandir does not alter Tyrion's Armour save.

Magic Items:
Sunfang (Magic Weapon)
This ancient sword, forged to do battle against the Daemons of Chaos burns with the captured fires of the sun. The white hot runes smouldering along its length contain incredible power and promise blazing ruin to its victims.

Once per battle in the Shooting phase, Tyrion may release the power within Sunfang, unleashing a fiery blast of magical power. This is a breath attack with a Strength of 4.

Sunfang also increases Tyrion's strength by +3 and inflicts Flaming Attacks.

Dragon Armour of Aenarion (Magic Armour)
This mighty armour was forged on Vaul's Anvil long ago to protect Aenarion, the first Phoenix King, in the great wars against Chaos. Upon Aenarion's death, his armour was thought lost for thousands of years, until it was recovered by Tethlis the Slayer.

The Dragon Armour gives Tyrion an Armour save of 1+, and a 4+ Ward save.

With the exception of this improved save, the Dragon Armour of Aenarion follows the normal rules for Dragon Armour on page 57.

Heart of Avelorn (Enchanted Item)
The Heart of Avelorn is a gift from the Everqueen to Tyrion that protects against evil magic. It is said that it also grants the bearer the power to cheat death.

The Heart of Avelorn gives Tyrion Magic Resistance (2). It also gives Tyrion the Regenerate special rule.

Prince Tyrion, Defender of Ulthuan and Champion of the Everqueen.

TECLIS

Twin to the mighty Tyrion, Teclis is wholly the opposite of his brother. Physically he is frail and must sustain himself by imbibing magical potions of his own creation. He is not a master of swordplay nor strategy. However, he is the greatest living Mage in this age of the world, and his mastery of the magical arts is unsurpassed by any other living creature. It is claimed that his power is on a par with the great Necromancer Nagash, so it is fortunate that Teclis has devoted his life to thwarting the powers of Chaos and death. It was Teclis who first taught Imperial wizards how to control the raging energies of the magical realm, and on his instruction the Colleges of Magic were established. It was only with the aid of Teclis that Magnus the Pious was able to push back the forces of the Dark Gods in the Great War against Chaos. Truly Teclis is one of those legendary heroes whose actions shape the world.

Teclis is a mage of prodigious power, able to stand against any other wizard in the world. With Teclis in your force, you will be able to unleash a magical assault that your opponents will be hard pressed to bear.

	M	WS	BS	S	T	W	I	A	LD
Teclis	5	3	3	2	2	3	5	1	10

Armour:
None.

Weapons:
The Sword of Teclis.

Special Rules:
Valour of Ages; Speed of Asuryan (see page 43).

High Loremaster: Teclis is the High Loremaster of Hoeth and many High Elves boast that he is the greatest living mage in the world.

Teclis is a Level 4 Wizard and may choose any one of the eight Lores of Magic or High Magic before the game starts. Whichever Lore he chooses, he knows all six spells.

In addition, any spell cast by Teclis will be cast with Irresistible Force on any successful casting roll which includes a double, except a Miscast.

Magic Items:
Sword of Teclis   **(Magic Weapon)**
This sword was forged by Teclis, a powerful weapon to protect himself as he began the perilous quest to rescue his brother Tyrion and the Everqueen.

All hits from the Sword of Teclis wound on a 2+. Armour saves may not be taken against this weapon.

Moon Staff of Lileath   **(Arcane Item)**
The Moon Staff of Lileath is imbued with the power of the goddess. This power flows through Teclis, invigorating his feeble frame and filling him with magical energy.

The Moon Staff gives Teclis D3 bonus power/dispel dice in each Magic phase.

War Crown of Saphery   **(Arcane Item)**
The War Crown is an ancient symbol of the magical realm of Saphery, seldom seen outside the walls of the White Tower unless in times of peril. It was gifted to Teclis by the former High Loremaster on the eve of the young mage's departure on the quest for his brother, Tyrion.

Teclis may ignore the effects of the first miscast he makes each turn. The spell is still a failure, but Teclis is able to dissipate the magical energies harmlessly and suffers no ill effects.

Scroll of Hoeth   **(Arcane Item)**
Though clearly ancient and seemingly fragile, this well-worn heirloom has seen a thousand battles and will see many more.

One use only. When the enemy casts a spell, Teclis may read the Scroll of Hoeth aloud as he might read a Dispel scroll and with the same effect. In addition, both Teclis and the caster roll a D6; if Teclis scores higher, the spell is removed from the mind of the caster and cannot be used for the rest of the battle.

The Blessings of Lileath
The Moon Staff is one of three sacred gifts bestowed upon the Elves by the goddess Lileath, the eternally young daughter of Isha.

It is many thousands of years since the gifts of Lileath were wielded as one, for the other gifts have long since been lost to the tides of ruin and war. The Star Crown, said to have granted the bearer vision of all times and places known to the gods, was shattered in Malekith's first assault on Saphery. To this day, the Loremasters of Hoeth search in desperation for the lost fragments of the Star Crown. Even the merest shard of the crown contains great power, and many an Elven mage dreams of harnessing that might to his own ends.

The Amulet of Sunfire was the second of Lileath's gifts. So bright and pure did it burn that no evil creature could bear its presence, whilst those beings who with truly noble hearts found in it a source of hope and vigour. Alas, the Amulet of Sunfire was lost forever in the depths of the Churning Gulf when the prince that bore it was thrown from the prow of his ship during a raging storm.

Teclis, the High Loremaster of Hoeth.

ALITH ANAR
THE SHADOW KING

There are many stories of Elven heroes of the Nagarythe from the time of the Sundering, of brave and valiant warriors, of remarkable deeds, and of battles against the darkest foes. The most popular tales concern Alith Anar, the Shadow King.

Alith Anar's adventures are shared throughout the courts of the Asur, each a tale of courageous defiance against Malekith and the Druchii. The tales of the Shadow King that stem from the years following the destruction of Anlec are, by now, undoubtedly a blend of fable and reality. It is impossible to say for sure which are true and which are invention, for the Nagarythe are understandably secretive about their history since the Sundering.

Alith Anar is an ideal choice for players who want a versatile and cost effective army leader. Armed with the Moonbow he shoots with the power of a Bolt Thrower, while offering close combat prowess as deadly as a High Elf Prince.

	M	WS	BS	S	T	W	I	A	LD
Alith Anar	5	7	7	4	3	3	9	4	10

Armour:
Light armour.

Weapons:
Hand weapon and the Moonbow.

Special Rules:
Valour of Ages; Speed of Asuryan (see page 43).
Nagarythe Hatred (see page 52).
Scout (see rule book).

Magic Items:
Stone of Midnight   **(Talisman)**
The Stone of Midnight was a gift to Morathi from Aenarion, the first and mightiest of the Phoenix kings. It was stolen from her palace by Alith Anar, who made mockery of the sorcerous wards that protected it, and deftly evaded the guardians of the Hag Queen. The Hag Sorceress has promised the gift of eternal youth and a night of debauchery with the most beautiful of her Witch Elves to whoever can return her treasure.

Alith Anar receives a 4+ Ward save. In addition, anyone shooting at Alith Anar (and the unit he is with) suffers an additional penalty of -1 on the roll to hit.

Shadow Crown   **(Enchanted Item)**
The Shadow Crown is the symbol of the rightful rulers of Nagarythe, a simple silver circlet set with a single diamond. The Witch King covets this crown greatly, for without the crown his claim to the throne of Nagarythe is hollow indeed. Thanks to the magic contained within the crown, Alith Anar has managed to escape death on scores of occasions. By speaking the name of his kingdom, and defiantly claiming his rulership, Alith Anar can freeze time for a blink of an eye, giving himself a brief instant to slip away from danger.

If Alith Anar (and any unit he is with) breaks from close combat, any opponents pursuing him must halve the distance they roll (rounding up) for pursuing.

Moonbow   **(Magic Weapon)**
The Moonbow is an exquisite weapon forged from a pale metal that glitters in the moonlight. The Shadow Warriors claim it was handed to Alith Anar by the goddess Lileath. This bow has been the bane of countless Dark Elves and its reputation is legendary. The merest whisper of the arrows shot by the Moonbow will strike fear into the hearts of the Druchii.

The Moonbow has a range of 36". Roll to hit as normal. Resolve a hit from this bow like a single bolt from a Bolt Thrower (see the Main rule book for details). Note that Alith Anar may shoot after moving (but not marching) and stand & shoot with the Moonbow as normal. Units of Dark Elves that suffer any casualties from the Moonbow must take a Panic test, exactly as if the unit had suffered 25% casualties.

ELTHARION THE GRIM
WARDEN OF TOR YVRESSE

Eltharion the Grim was one of the greatest of all Elven lords, the son of the noblest stock and a superb warrior. He is the only High Elf commander to launch a successful attack on the city of Naggarond itself, an action that earned him the lasting enmity of the Witch King. At the height of his glory, Eltharion commanded a mighty army and it was under his leadership that Waaagh! Grom was finally defeated. For his valour in that battle, Eltharion was elected as the Warden of Tor Yvresse and though he was a dour, forbidding ruler, the people of that fair city loved their grim guardian.

Eltharion is a consummate warrior, an excellent general and also, thanks to the Talisman of Hoeth, a Sorceror of significant ability. He offers the High Elf player the perfect compromise between warrior, wizard and leader.

	M	WS	BS	S	T	W	I	A	LD
Eltharion	5	8	6	4	3	3	8	4	10
Stormwing	6	6	0	5	5	5	7	4	8

Armour:
Heavy armour and the Helm of Yvresse

Weapons:
The Fangsword of Eltharion and a longbow.

Mount:
Eltharion may ride his Griffon, Stormwing.

Special Rules:
Valour of Ages; Speed of Asuryan (see page 43).
Hates all Goblins (see rule book).

Blood Oath: Grom the Paunch of Misty Mountain led the Waaagh! that ravaged much of Yvresse, wiping out almost all of Eltharion's family and leaving his ancestral lands burned and defiled. Few feel a hate as intense as the utter loathing Eltharion reserves for Grom.

Such is Eltharion's hatred of the Goblin Warlord Grom that, in addition to Hating him (as per the main rule book), Eltharion receives +1 To Hit and +1 Strength when rolling to attack Grom in close combat.

Magic Items:
The Fangsword of Eltharion   (Magic Weapon)
Eltharion always wields the Fangsword in combat, striking down his foes from the back of his faithful mount Stormwing. The Fangsword is a rune-encrusted longsword which has been passed down through Eltharion's family for generations.

No armour saves can be taken against wounds caused by the Fangsword of Eltharion. In addition, it grants the wielder +2 Strength on the turn he charges.

The Helm of Yvresse   (Magic Armour)
The Helm of Yvresse is the symbol of the Warden of Yvresse. Made from shining ithilmar and gold, and decorated with majestic feathers, the Helm of Yvresse provides protection from harm, as well as embuing the wearer with a clarity of thought unmatched by mere mortals.

The Helm of Yvresse adds +1 to Eltharion's Armour save, for a total Armour save of 4+. In addition while he is alive, Eltharion and Stormwing receive a 5+ Ward save.

Talisman of Hoeth   (Enchanted Item)
Created by the first Warden of Tor Yvresse, a mighty and wise sorceror, the Talisman of Hoeth allows its wearer a measure of the original Warden's knowledge. Any who wear the Talisman of Hoeth find themselves embued with incredible magical powers, able to command the Winds of Magic as if born to it.

This item makes Eltharion a Level 2 High Elf Mage, who can choose any one of the eight Lores of Magic found in the Warhammer rule book.

KORHIL
CAPTAIN OF THE WHITE LIONS

When the Captain of the White Lions met his death at the hands of the Dark Elf Assassin Urian Poisonblade, the bodyguard of the Phoenix King gathered to select a new leader from amongst their ranks. Their choice, approved and blessed by the Phoenix King, was the warrior Korhil.

It was Korhil who hunted and caught the great lion Charandis. This lion was a particularly dangerous, massive and ferocious creature, mutated by the warping power of Chaos that seeps from the magic-riven Annulii mountains. Already dozens of High Elf warriors and scores of innocents had been slain by the mighty beast when the young Korhil encountered it. By his wits and skill alone he survived the beast's attacks long enough to realise that the blows from his woodsman's axe had no effect on Charandis's magical hide so, in a feat of physical strength unheard of for an Elf, he wrestled the raging beast to the ground and throttled the life from its thrashing body.

The White Lions claim Korhil to be the mightiest Elf in all of Ulthuan, and certainly his strength and stature is legendary. Yet, Korhil is no lumbering giant, for he wields his long axe with dexterity and grace that makes even his fellow White Lions appear cumbersome. His honest demeanour and noble bearing have won him many friends among the Lords of Ulthuan and other races besides.

Korhil has served his Lord, Phoenix King Finubar the Seafarer, with unfailing loyalty for many years, standing steadfastly beside him. Most notably during the Battle of Tor Achare where he saved Finubar's life, disembowling the Manticore ridden by Morech the Black.

Such is Korhil's integrity, and the trust that Finubar places in him, that the Captain of the White Lions has led the armies of the Phoenix King on a number of occasions, acting as both Finubar's champion and general.

	M	WS	BS	S	T	W	I	A	LD
Korhil	5	6	6	4	3	2	7	3	9

Armour:
Heavy armour, Pelt of Charandis.

Weapons:
Hand weapon and Chayal.

Special Rules:
Valour of Ages; Speed of Asuryan (see page 43).
Woodsman (see page 58).
Stubborn (see rule book for details).

Magic Items:
Chayal   (Magic Weapon)
Chayal is a unique magic weapon, carried by the Captain of the White Lions since their founding. Lighter than a child's wooden toy, a warrior of sufficient skill can wield Chayal with incredible speed, effortlessly hacking off heads and limbs with every stroke.

Chayal gives the wielder +2 strength and the Killing Blow special rule.

Pelt of Charandis   (Magic Armour)
When Korhil slew the Great Lion Charandis he afterwards skinned the animal and wore its fur proudly upon his broad shoulders. Years later it was remade into a magnificent cloak, enchanted by the Loremaster Finreir and presented to Korhil as a gift from Finubar himself.

The cloak increases Korhil's armour save to 4+ against close combat attacks and 3+ against shooting attacks. In addition, Korhil is immune to poison, whatever its source.

CARADRYAN
CAPTAIN OF THE PHOENIX GUARD

Caradryan was an arrogant lordling in his youth. Handsome, rich, powerful and conceited he was the very archetype of the jaded High Elf aristocrat. Caradryan's life changed when he made a pilgrimage to the Shrine of Asuryan, a journey which all High Elf nobles are expected to undertake at least once. There, in perhaps the worst display of arrogance in his life, Caradryan allowed his curiosity to overcome his good judgement and sneaked into the holy Chamber of Days. What he witnessed there no-one knows, but when he emerged he was a changed man. On his forehead was the glowing rune of Asuryan, marking him as the servant of the Creator God. Why Asuryan had chosen Caradryan as the instrument of his will is unknown but Caradryan gave up all

his worldly possessions and took the vows of the Phoenix Guard that same day, and has not uttered a word ever since.

Caradryan spends his days in meditation in the Chamber of Days, reading the fiery letters that tell of the past, the present and the future. During the years he has become ever closer to the thoughts of Asuryan, until he was marked as the Captain of the Phoenix Guard by the ancient Elf god. Now he leads the Phoenix Guard during times of peace and war, taking orders from no worldly master and appearing on the battlefield only by the will of Asuryan. He serves the purpose and the plan of the Lord of the Gods. There is strength in his hand, and the wisdom of Asuryan sits on his noble brow.

A good fighter, who is able to shrug off the worst enemy magic, Caradryan is a sound choice to give extra punch to your Phoenix Guard or even lead a smaller High Elf force into battle.

	M	WS	BS	S	T	W	I	A	LD
Caradryan	5	6	6	4	3	2	7	3	9

Armour:
Heavy armour.

Weapons:
The Phoenix Blade.

Special Rules:
Valour of Ages; Speed of Asuryan (see page 43).
Cause Fear; Magic Resistance (3);
4+ Ward Save (see rule book).

Mark of Asuryan: *Though Caradryan has taken a strict vow of silence, he is privileged to know the secret words that will unleash the fury of Asuryan. Should he suffer a mortal blow, he will call upon the Lord of the Gods to avenge him.*

If Caradryan is killed in close combat, he will speak for one final time and call on Asuryan to visit his wrath upon Caradryan's slayer. The model that killed Caradryan immediately suffers D6 wounds, with no armour save allowed.

Magic Items:
The Phoenix Blade   **(Magic Weapon)**
This ancient halberd was enchanted for the Captain of the Phoenix Guard Kor-Baelan.

All attacks made with the Phoenix Blade are flaming attacks. In addition, it causes not one but D3 wounds against enemy models with Unit Strength 2 or greater.

COLLECTING A HIGH ELF ARMY

The High Elf army is one of the deadliest in the Warhammer world, ideal for veteran gamers and beginners alike. Seasoned High Elf commander and author of this army book, Adam Troke offers some words of advice for collecting your own High Elf force.

Getting Started

A good place to aim when you start a Warhammer army is a force of about 1,000 points. An army of this size isn't too intimidating for new players to collect, and can provide hours of entertaining battles.

The first thing every army needs is a hero to lead it into battle. For the High Elves you can choose between a Noble, a Mage, or a Dragon Mage. Nobles are excellent generals, and benefit from a high Leadership value, as well as being skilled in close combat. Mages aren't quite as good at commanding a large force, and they're not going to win many close combats. They are, however, among the best wizards in Warhammer. High Elf Mages can stop the worst of your opponent's spells, and can keep your army safe on its way into battle, as well as blasting your foes into cinders, summoning the wrath of Khaine upon the enemy. Dragon Mages are an exciting option, combining barely controlled fiery magic with the awesome power of a Dragon and, when using the Flaming Sword of Rhuin spell which they can always choose, possess excellent close combat ability.

The Core of your Army

With your army general selected, you'll want to pick a solid block of troops for him to lead. All High Elf armies are built around regiments of Spearmen and Archers, the valiant infantry who form the mainstay of Ulthuan's military might. Since all High Elf warriors, even the Core troops, are skilled fighters you can't go too far wrong. I usually start with Spearmen. Units of 15 to 20 models are about right in my experience. They benefit from a healthy rank bonus in combat and they're able to fight with more models than similar enemy units.

A unit or two of Archers are great to inflict casualties from afar - their longbows and high Ballistic Skill means they can outshoot many foes. Choosing two or more small units of ten Archers allows you real versatility and manoeuvrability. They can either stand back and support your army from long range, or advance with the force, keeping up a withering hail of fire.

It's also worth looking at the Lothern Sea Guard. They're my favourite High Elf Core unit, because they're so well equipped. They have bows and spears, which gives them the best of both worlds. Of course, because they're so flexible Sea Guard cost more points, so you can't fit as many of them into your force. Still, I normally treat myself to a unit or two of 15 Sea Guard to form the backbone of my High Elf army.

Special Requests

One thing that sets the High Elves apart from other Warhammer armies is the number of Special choices that their armies can include - typically two more than other armies. This means you can include a real variety of Special troops in your army, which is appropriate for the legendary hosts of Ulthuan.

The High Elves have excellent specialist troops – something for every situation to be honest. Most High Elf players choose their specialist units based solely on which ones they like the look of most, and that's the rule of thumb I use too. I love to include a regiment of Phoenix Guard in my force whenever I can, because the models are some of my favourites, but also because they've got a few special rules that really help out. They cause fear (which is great against armies with a low Leadership) and they've also got a 4+ Ward save. The Lion Chariot looks amazing and on the charge it inflicts impact hits followed by attacks from the great weapon-armed crew and four Strength 5 attacks from the Lions – a fearsome prospect that's hard to pass up!

There are other Special choices I've not mentioned though, and each has their own advantages. The Sword Masters are probably the most skilled infantry in the whole Warhammer game, while the Dragon Princes of Caledor vie for the honour of the finest heavy cavalry. Then there are White Lions, Silver Helms, Ellyrian Reavers, Shadow Warriors and Tiranoc Chariots all with their own merits. If you pick the ones you like the most, you won't go far wrong.

Rare Gems

The High Elf army also allows you to choose extra Rare units. These tend to be very powerful or influential playing pieces. Bolt Throwers can unleash firepower that is unequalled in the High Elf army and are best used to thin out the ranks of the foe - tackling heavily armoured regiments and mighty beasts with its bolts. Great Eagles are best suited to disrupting the movement of enemy troops and picking off the crew of enemy war machines.

The following pages display the High Elf army, as painted by the 'Eavy Metal team, and will serve as inspiration for your own new army, or for additions to an existing High Elf force.

BUILDING YOUR FORCE

This 1,000 point army is built using the High Elf Battalion boxed set, along with a Noble to lead the force and a unit of the legendary Sword Masters. A force like this is an ideal starting point for a High Elf player and provides a great building block for a larger army.

Using the first army as the basis for a larger force, this is a 2,000 point army. The additions include powerful heroes – a Dragon Mage, a level 2 Mage and a Battle Standard Bearer. The new units are skirmishing Shadow Warriors and a hard-hitting strike force of chariots.

HIGH ELF COMMANDERS

Prince on Star Dragon

The ancient Dragons of Ulthuan will occasionally awaken to bear a great Prince or Archmage into battle, breathing gouts of flame and decimating whole regiments of the foe.

Heavy armour and scales turn aside enemy blows.

▲ **High Elf Commanders**
Princes and Nobles lead the High Elves to war.

▲ **Noble with Battle Standard**
Bearing the Phoenix Banner.

Tyrion,
The Defender of Ulthuan
Champion of the Everqueen,
wielder of the magical sword
Sunfang and wearer of the
Heart of Avelorn.

▲ *The Princes and Nobles*
of Ulthuan often
honour the ancient
Dragons in the style of
their armour and
detailing on their cloaks.

▲ **High Elf Commander**
Riding Elven Steed.

▲ *Eltharion rides to war*
atop the mighty Griffon
Stormwing, who has
saved the Elf Lord's life
on many occasions.

▲ *Eltharion's long bow is*
stowed behind his saddle.

▲ **Eltharion the Grim**
Warden of Tor Yvresse.

HIGH ELF WARRIORS

Hawkeye
The champions of Archer regiments are veterans of countless battles.

Archers
All High Elves wear white robes, decorated with a second colour. For our army we have chosen blue for this accent colour.

Spearman
This model has been painted with purple as the accent colour.

Archer
With longbow.

Archer
Turquoise has been used instead of blue on this model.

Sentinel
The champions of Spearman regiments are known as Sentinels.

Spearmen
The armour of the High Elves is gleaming silver.

Sentinel
The skilled champion of a Spearman regiment.

SENTINELS OF THE COAST

Lothern Sea Guard
The versatile Sea Guard carry both spears and bows into battle.

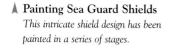

Painting Sea Guard Shields
This intricate shield design has been painted in a series of stages.

Sea Master
Sea Guard champions are battle-hardened professional soldiers.

Sea Guard
Wearing the livery of Sea Lord Aislinn.

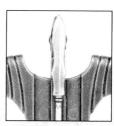

Repeater Bolt Thrower
Crewed by grim Lothern Sea Guard, Eagle Claw Bolt Throwers guard the cliffs and cities of Ulthuan.

A leaf-bladed bolt, ideal for piercing ranks of enemy troops.

THE RIDERS OF ULTHUAN

> **Silver Helms**
> *Impetuous young nobles, keen
> to prove their battle prowess.*

△ High Helm
Champion of the Sliver Helms.

△ Tiranoc Chariots and Ellyrian Reavers
Deadly Tiranoc chariots, crewed by skilled High Elf warriors, flank a unit of Ellyrian Reavers.

WARDENS OF THE WILDS

Shadow Warriors spend days at a time stealthily hunting their prey through the wilds, carrying ammunition and supplies on their backs.

Alith Anar
The Shadow King of Nagarythe.

Arrows shot with the Moonbow have the power to pierce many ranks of enemy troops

Shadow Warriors
The embittered Elves of Nagarythe hold a special hatred for their cousins, the Dark Elves.

Shadow-walker
Determined champion of the Shadow Warriors.

Tiranoc Charioteers are armed with spears and bows.

LOREMASTERS OF HOETH

▲ **Teclis, High Loremaster**
The mightiest living mage in all of the world, bearer of the Moon Staff of Lileath and the War Crown of Saphery.

▲ **Mage on Elven steed**
The Mages of Saphery use enchanted staffs to focus their powers

▲► **High Elf Mages**

▲ *Tomes of arcane power and ancient magical staffs contain spells to blast the foes of Ulthuan.*

▲► **Sword Masters of Hoeth**
Ulthuan's most deadly warriors, the Sword Masters are the mystic guardians of the White Tower.

THE LORDS OF CALEDOR

Dragon Mages fight wielding sunstaffs alight with magical flame.

▲ **Dragon Mage of Caledor**

The warlike Dragon Mages add their own fiery magic to the burning breath of their Sun Dragon mounts.

▲ **Drakemaster**
Proud champion of the Dragon Princes.

▲ **Dragon Princes of Caledor**
A Dragon Prince can slay two warriors with one thrust of his lance.

▲ *Dragon Prince shield.*

THE WHITE LIONS OF CHRACE

▲ Korhil, Captain of
the White Lions

▲ Korhil wears the
Pelt of Charandis.

▲ **White Lions**
The White Lion regiments serve as the Phoenix King's bodyguard.

◄ The chariot's open
siding allows the
White Lions to fight
with their great axes.

▲ **Lion Chariot of Chrace**
Few enemy regiments can withstand
the ferocious charge of a Lion Chariot.

▲ A War Lion's mane is
never shorn, but rather
plaited and decorated.

THE PHOENIX GUARD

▲ **Phoenix Guard**
The legions of the Phoenix Guard defend the fabled Shrine of Asuryan.

▲ *Flames and the Phoenix are the sacred icons of Asuryan.*

◀▲ **Caradryan**
The Captain of the Phoenix Guard bears the mark of Asuryan on his brow.

◀▲ **Keeper of the Flame**
This Phoenix Guard champion has been painted with an alternative colour scheme, including an intricate flame pattern on the cloak.

Painting Gemstones

Many High Elf warriors display gems on their weapons and armour. Gemstones can simply be painted a flat colour and given a coat of gloss varnish. Alternatively you could try this colour scheme using the steps shown here:

1
● *Blood Red*

2
● *Red Gore*

3
● *Fiery Orange*

4
○ *Skull White*

HIGH ELF BANNERS

Each banner and battle standard taken to war by the High Elves is an intricately designed masterpiece, crafted with years of care and attention. They are woven from luxurious silken threads and depict symbols and runes that represent High Elf mythology.

Once a High Elf army has arrayed for war, it is traditional for all banners upon the field of battle to be lowered, showing fealty to the Phoenix King. No banner bearer would dare to let his standard touch the floor however, for that is considered an act of grave dishonour.

▲ **Infantry Banners**
High Elf infantry regiments typically bear gonfalons style banners, that are supported horizontally from a cross piece. The banners shown here depict heraldic designs set against the night sky.

◀ **Cavalry Banners**
Cavalry regiments carry traditional battle flags attached to a vertical pole.

▲ **Pennants**
Pennants can be fixed to spears or lances on cavalry models. Each bears some form of icon or rune.

➤ **Chariot Banner**
High Elf charioteers take great pride in their banners. This Chracian flag bears the rune Charoi, signifying ferocity.

▲ *This intricate design was carefully hand painted onto a paper banner.*

▲ *This High Elf Battle Standard Bearer carries the Banner of the World Dragon.*

HIGH ELF SHIELDS

Every High Elf warrior who carries a shield into battle bears the responsibility for decorating it in accordance with the traditions of his regiment. They vary from ornate designs to simple runes (which are explained over the page).

The High Elf nobility typically bear shields with designs that are entirely unique to them, each an individually crafted masterpiece.

This intricately detailed shield commemorates a bloody victory.

This shield bears the heraldry of King Finubar the Seafarer.

The Elves of Nagarythe favour a black field for their shields.

This symbol was borne by Caradinor against the Daemons.

One of the shields common among the armies of Saphery.

Many Reaver Knights display this striking emblem.

The white lion is often displayed by Spearmen and Silver Helms from Chrace.

This design is associated with Tethlis the Slayer.

Many spearmen of Hoeth bear shields with this pattern.

A design often adopted by regiments whose champion has been slain.

◀ *This shield is edged with elaborate gold filigree.*

▶ *A stooping sea hawk is the symbol of Sea Lord Aislinn.*

▲ *The wealthiest nobles have elegant designs sculpted on their shields.*

▲ **Sea Guard**
This regiment has had their shields painted in the personal colours of Sea Lord Aislinn.

HIGH ELF RUNES

The ancient runescript of the High Elves is the most refined form of writing in the world. For eight thousand years the High Elves have developed their runes and signs so they could be used to store their accumulated knowledge and safeguard their songs and history for future generations.

High Elves frequently decorate their standards, weapons and armour with runes. The runes used in war often represent the pride and might of the High Elves, but also remind them of the noble principles of Elven warfare. Many High Elf standards are magical and their runes form a glowing, swirling pattern that creates otherworldly visions to embolden the High Elves and terrify their foes. Likewise, shields and even the robes of individual warriors or mages are frequently adorned with runes, either magical or mundane. For a High Elf there is great spiritual value in bearing a rune that proclaims loyalty or threatens death to the enemies of Ulthuan.

▲ *Runes are easier to paint on the large, flat areas of models.*

▲ *This High Elf champion has been lavishly decorated with dozens of hand-painted runes and patterns.*

▲ *Note the rune-pattern repeated along the hem.*

Sarathai
The rune of the World Dragon, symbolising defiance, unyielding.

Charoi
Strength, ferocity, mane of hair.

Arhain
Shadows, night, stealth, secrets, perfidiousness.

Daroir
Remembrance, memory, the strength of stones.

Sariour
The moon, magic, fortune, evil deeds, destruction wrought by nature.

Yenlui
Balance, harmony, Chaos.

Quyl-Isha
The tears of Isha, sorrow, mercy, endurance, mourning for lost children.

Lathain
Storm, wrath, gently falling rain that brings eternal sleep.

Elui
Ending or denial.

Saroir
Eternity, infinity, the flame of love that burns all it touches.

Ceyl
Law, order, justice, passion, sword that draws blood.

Cynath
Chill, death, silence, loneliness.

Menlui
Water, life, majesty, weakness, torrential rain and thunder in distant mountains.

Caladai
Symbol of the line of kings, the dragons of flame.

Senlui
Swiftness, accuracy.

Cython
The serpent, wisdom, knowledge, futility, the symbol of Lileath.

Thalui
Hatred or vengeance.

Senthoi
Unity, loyalty, broken promise.

Elthrai
Doom, inexorable fate, hope.

Cadaith
Grace, power, music of the stars.

Harathoi
Youth, boundless energy, jealousy.

Lecai
Light, nobility of the soul, lightness of being.

Thanan
Hidden power, inner strength, indecisiveness.

Asur
The eternal flame, Mark of Asuryan, symbol of rebirth and lordship.

Urithair
Destruction, conquest, sacrifice of innocence.

Minaith
Skill in arms, spirituality, the Lost Way.

Lacoi
Might, glory, fear of death.

Oriour
Blood, birth.

Sethai
Flight, wind, cry in the far mountains.

HIGH ELF ARMY LIST

This army list enables you to turn your Citadel miniatures collection into an army ready for a tabletop battle. As described in the Warhammer rule book, the army list is divided into four sections: Characters (including Lords and Heroes), Core Units, Special Units and Rare Units.

Choosing an Army

Every miniature in the Warhammer range has a points cost that reflects how effective it is on the battlefield. For example, a High Elf Spearman costs just 9 points, while a mighty High Elf Archmage costs 225 points!

Both players choose armies to the same agreed points total. You can spend less and will probably find it impossible to use up every last point. Most "2,000 point" armies, for example, will be something like 1,998 or 1,999 points.

To form your miniatures into an army, look up the relevant army list entry for the first troop type. This tells you the points cost to add each unit of models to your army and any options or upgrades the unit may have. Then select your next unit, calculate its points and so on until you reach the agreed points total. In addition to the points value, there are a few other rules that govern which units you can include in your army, as detailed under Choosing Characters and Choosing Troops.

Army List Entries

Profiles. The characteristic profiles for the model(s) in each unit are provided as a reminder. Where several profiles are required, these are also given even if they are optional.

Unit Size. Each troop entry specifies the minimum size for each unit, which is the smallest number of models needed to form that unit. In some cases units also have a maximum size.

Equipment. Each entry lists the standard weapons and armour for that unit type. The cost of these items is included in the basic points value. Additional or optional weapons and armour cost extra and are covered in the Options section of the unit entry.

Special Rules. Many troops have special rules that are fully described earlier in this book. The names of these rules are listed as a reminder.

Options. Many entries list different weapon, armour and equipment options, along with any additional points cost for giving them to the unit. This includes magic items and other upgrades for characters. It may also include the option to upgrade a unit member to a champion, standard bearer or musician.

Choosing Characters

Characters are divided into two categories: Lords and Heroes. The maximum number of characters an army can include is shown on the chart below. Of these, only a certain number can be Lords.

Army Points Value	Max. Total	Max. Lords	Max. Heroes
Less than 2,000	3	0	3
2,000 or more	4	1	4
3,000 or more	6	2	6
4,000 or more	8	3	8
Each +1,000	+2	+1	+2

An army must always include at least one character to act as the general. If you include more than one character, then the one with the highest Leadership value is the general. When one or more characters have the same (and highest) Leadership, choose one to be the general at the start of the battle. Make sure that your opponent knows which character is your general when you deploy your army.

Many High Elf characters can be equipped with Magic Items from Vaul's Forge. These items range from powerful magical weapons, to banners and other arcane items. Where characters have this option, it is included in their profile.

Choosing Troops

The number of each type of unit allowed depends on the army's points value. Note that the number of Special and Rare units permitted is greater than the normal allowance for other armies.

Army Points Value	Core	Special	Rare
Less than 2,000	1+	0-5	0-2
2,000 or more	2+	0-6	0-4
3,000 or more	3+	0-7	0-6
4,000 or more	4+	0-8	0-8
Each +1,000	+ 1 minimum	+0-1	+0-2

Like many characters, some High Elf units can be equipped with magic items from Vaul's Forge (normally banners, although some unit champions can carry other items). Where units have this option, it is included in their profile.

LORDS

Tyrion

Points/model: 400

	M	WS	BS	S	T	W	I	A	LD
Tyrion	5	9	7	4	3	4	10	4	10
Malhandir	10	4	0	4	3	1	5	2	7

Your army can only include one Tyrion model.

Equipment:
- Dragon Armour of Aenarion
- Sunfang
- Heart of Avelorn

Mount:
Malhandir

Special Rules:
- Valour of Ages
- Speed of Asuryan
- Defender of Ulthuan

Teclis

Points/model: 475

	M	WS	BS	S	T	W	I	A	LD
Teclis	5	3	3	2	2	3	5	1	10

Your army can only include one Teclis model.

Magic:
Teclis is a Level 4 Wizard. He may choose either High Magic or any of the eight lores described in the Warhammer rule book.

Equipment:
- Sword of Teclis
- Moon Staff of Lileath
- Scroll of Hoeth
- War Crown of Saphery

Special Rules:
- Valour of Ages
- Speed of Asuryan
- High Loremaster

Eltharion

Points/model: 285

	M	WS	BS	S	T	W	I	A	LD
Eltharion	5	8	6	4	3	3	8	4	10
Stormwing	6	6	0	5	5	5	7	4	8

Your army can only include one Eltharion model.

Equipment:
- Heavy armour
- Longbow
- The Fangsword of Eltharion
- The Helm of Yvresse
- Talisman of Hoeth

Mount:
May ride Stormwing for 205 points

Special Rules:
- Valour of Ages
- Speed of Asuryan
- Hates Goblins
- Blood Oath

Alith Anar

Points/model: 245

	M	WS	BS	S	T	W	I	A	LD
Alith Anar	5	7	7	4	3	3	9	4	10

Your army can only include one Alith Anar model.

Equipment:
- Hand weapon
- Light armour
- The Moonbow
- The Shadow Crown
- The Stone of Midnight

Special Rules:
- Valour of Ages
- Speed of Asuryan
- Nagarythe Hatred
- Scout

LORDS

Prince

	M	WS	BS	S	T	W	I	A	LD
Prince	5	7	6	4	3	3	8	4	10

Weapons & Armour:
Hand weapon

Special Rules:
- Valour of Ages
- Speed of Asuryan

Points/model: 150

Options:

Weapons (one choice only):
Lance 6pts
Spear 3pts
Great weapon 12pts
Halberd 6pts
Additional hand weapon 6pts

Armour (one choice only):
Light armour 3pts
Heavy armour 6pts
Dragon armour 9pts

Magic items:
Any, up to a total of . . 100pts

Mount (one choice only):
Elven steed 18pts
Barded Elven steed 24pts
Great Eagle 50pts
Griffon 200pts
Sun Dragon 230pts
Moon Dragon 300pts
Star Dragon 370pts
Tiranoc Chariot 85pts
  (replaces one of the crew)

Additional Equipment:
Shield 3pts
Longbow 10pts

Archmage

	M	WS	BS	S	T	W	I	A	LD
Archmage	5	4	4	3	3	3	5	1	9

Weapons & Armour:
- Hand weapon

Special Rules:
- Valour of Ages
- Speed of Asuryan

Magic:
- An Archmage is a Level 3 Wizard. He may choose either High Magic or any of the eight lores described in the Warhammer rule book.

Points/model: 225

Options:

Upgrade:
To a Level 4 Wizard 35pts

Magic items:
Any, up to a total of . . 100pts

Mount (one choice only):
Elven steed 18pts
Barded Elven steed 24pts
Great Eagle 50pts
Sun Dragon 250pts
Moon Dragon 300pts
Tiranoc Chariot 85pts
  (replaces one of the crew)

The stench of the Orc and Goblin horde was almost overwhelming, and Eolaran had to choke back the bile that rose unbidden in his throat. At the feet of his Sea Guard regiment, three score of the hulking Orcish warriors lay butchered, their corpses stinking of blood, mud and offal. Around him, the warriors of his regiment swiftly stowed their spears and restrung their bows, before unleashing a steady rain of arrows, harrying the distant Goblins.

The whole High Elf battle line was slowly advancing in the face of the Greenskins, the expert soldiers of Ulthuan proving more than a match for the undisciplined brutality of the Orcs. On the extreme right flank a large band of Orcs riding upon bloodthirsty boars had threatened to overwhelm several of the Spear regiments, but just as the citizen warriors had wavered, Lord Aislinn had charged into the fray upon his ferocious blue-white Dragon. With great gouts of flame and flashing jaws the mighty wyrm had ravaged the Greenskins and the survivors had broken and fled.

The distant formations of Goblins were firing occasional volleys of short, black arrows at the advancing Elves but they were a poor match for the skilled High Elf archers who returned fire. At this distance only enemy war machines threatened the Sea Guard. A bolt had skewered two of Eolaran's warriors with a lucky hit, and he had seen several Silver Helms literally smashed apart by a crashing boulder hurled by a stone thrower. Eolaran heard Lord Aislinn give the order to advance and as one the High Elves broke into an even, measured pace. Ellyrion Reavers raced ahead of the army, drawing out Orcs into positions where Silver Helms or Dragon Princes could ride them down. On the left flank the mysterious Sword Masters were fighting a swirling mêlée against a vast horde of Orcs clad in thick, black armour.

"Forward brothers!" Eolaran called to his Sea Guard. As one, they began to charge. Over their heads flew flights of arrows and bolts, and Eolaran felt his heart soar. The Asur were going to war - what foe could possibly stand against them!

HEROES

Caradryan

	M	WS	BS	S	T	W	I	A	LD
Caradryan	5	6	6	4	3	2	7	3	9

Your army can only include one Caradryan model.

Points/model: 175

Weapons & Armour:
- The Phoenix Blade
- Heavy armour

Special Rules:
- Valour of Ages
- Speed of Asuryan
- Causes *fear*
- Magic Resistance (3)
- Mark of Asuryan
- 4+ Ward Save

Korhil

	M	WS	BS	S	T	W	I	A	LD
Korhil	5	6	6	4	3	2	7	3	9

Your army can only include one Korhil model.

Weapons & Armour:
- Heavy armour
- Chayal
- Pelt of Charandis

Special Rules:
- Valour of Ages
- Speed of Asuryan
- Woodsmen
- Stubborn

Points/model: 140

Options:

Mount:
Lion Chariot 130pts
(replacing one of the crew)

Noble

	M	WS	BS	S	T	W	I	A	LD
Noble	5	6	6	4	3	2	7	3	9

Weapons & Armour:
- Hand weapon

Special Rules:
- Valour of Ages
- Speed of Asuryan

Points/model: 85

Options:

Weapons (one choice only):
Lance 4pts
Spear 2pts
Great weapon 8pts
Halberd 4pts
Additional hand weapon 4pts

Armour (one choice only):
Light armour 2pts
Heavy armour 4pts
Dragon armour 6pts

Mount (one choice only):
Elven steed 12pts
Barded Elven steed 16pts
Great Eagle 50pts
Tiranoc Chariot 85pts
(replaces one of the crew)

Additional Equipment:
Shield 2pts
Longbow 10pts

Magic items:
Any, up to a total of . . . 50pts

Battle Standard Bearer:
- One Noble in the army may carry the Battle Standard for +25 points. The Battle Standard Bearer may not be the army's general.

- The Battle Standard Bearer can have any magic banner (no points limit), but if he carries a magic banner he cannot carry any other magic items.

HEROES

Mage

Points/model: 100

	M	WS	BS	S	T	W	I	A	LD
Mage	5	4	4	3	3	2	5	1	8

Weapons & Armour:
- Hand weapon

Special Rules:
- Valour of Ages
- Speed of Asuryan

Magic: A Mage is a Level 1 Wizard. He may choose either High Magic or any of the eight lores described in the Warhammer rule book.

Options:

Upgrade:
To a Level 2 Wizard **35pts**

Mount (one choice only):
Elven steed **12pts**
Barded Elven steed **16pts**
Tiranoc Chariot **85pts**
    (replaces one of the crew)

Magic items:
Any, up to a total of . . . **50pts**

Dragon Mage of Caledor

Points/model: 350

	M	WS	BS	S	T	W	I	A	LD
Dragon Mage	5	4	4	3	3	2	6	2	8

Weapons & Armour:
- Hand weapon

Mount:
- Sun Dragon

Special Rules:
- Valour of Ages
- Speed of Asuryan
- Reckless
- Warrior Mage

Magic: A Dragon Mage is a Level 1 Wizard and always uses the Lore of Fire as described in the Warhammer rule book.

Options:

Upgrade:
To a Level 2 Wizard **35pts**

Magic items:
Any, up to a total of . . . **50pts**

Lords' and Heroes' Mounts

	M	WS	BS	S	T	W	I	A	LD
Elven Steed	9	3	0	3	3	1	4	1	5
Great Eagle	2	5	0	4	4	3	4	2	8
Griffon	6	5	0	5	5	4	5	4	7
Sun Dragon	6	5	0	5	6	5	4	4	7
Moon Dragon	6	6	0	6	6	6	3	5	8
Star Dragon	6	7	0	7	6	7	2	6	9

- Any Dragon (including the Sun Dragon ridden by a Dragon Mage) will take up an additional Hero slot.

- Tiranoc Chariots are described on page 97.

CORE

Archers

Points/model: 11

	M	WS	BS	S	T	W	I	A	LD
Archer	5	4	4	3	3	1	5	1	8
Hawkeye	5	4	5	3	3	1	5	1	8

Unit Size:
10+

Weapons & Armour:
• Hand weapon
• Longbow

Special Rules:
• Valour of Ages
• Speed of Asuryan

Options:

Command:
Upgrade one Archer to a Hawkeye 10pts
Upgrade one Archer to a Musician 5pts
Upgrade one Archer to a Standard Bearer 10pts

Additional equipment:
Light Armour . . . . 1pt per model

Spearmen

Points/model: 9

	M	WS	BS	S	T	W	I	A	LD
Spearman	5	4	4	3	3	1	5	1	8
Sentinel	5	4	4	3	3	1	5	2	8

Unit Size:
10+

Weapons & Armour:
• Hand weapon
• Spear
• Light armour
• Shield

Special Rules:
• Valour of Ages
• Speed of Asuryan
• Martial Prowess

Options:

Command:

Upgrade one Spearman to a Sentinel 10pts
Upgrade one Spearman to a Musician 5pts
Upgrade one Spearman to a Standard Bearer 10pts

---

Lothern Sea Guard

Points/model: 12

	M	WS	BS	S	T	W	I	A	LD
Sea Guard	5	4	4	3	3	1	5	1	8
Sea Master	5	4	4	3	3	1	5	2	8

Unit Size:
10+

Weapons & Armour:
• Hand weapon
• Spear
• Bow
• Light armour

Special Rules:
• Valour of Ages
• Speed of Asuryan
• Martial Prowess

Options:

Command:
Upgrade one Sea Guard to a Sea Master 10pts
Upgrade one Sea Guard to a Musician 5pts
Upgrade one Sea Guard to a Standard Bearer 10pts

Additional equipment:
Shield . . . . 1pt per model

First Among Equals

A single Core unit in the army may be given a magic standard worth up to 25 points.

SPECIAL

Sword Masters of Hoeth

Points/model: 15

	M	WS	BS	S	T	W	I	A	LD
Sword Master	5	6	4	3	3	1	5	2	8
Bladelord	5	6	4	3	3	1	5	3	8

Unit Size:
5+

Weapons & Armour:
- Two-handed sword (Great weapon)
- Hand weapon
- Heavy armour

Special Rules:
- Valour of Ages
- Speed of Asuryan

Options:

Command:
Upgrade one Sword Master to a Bladelord **12pts**
  Bladelord may have magic items worth up to **25pts**
Upgrade one Sword Master to a Musician **6pts**
Upgrade one Sword Master to a Standard Bearer **12pts**
  Standard Bearer may have a magic standard worth up to . .**50pts**

Phoenix Guard

Points/model: 15

	M	WS	BS	S	T	W	I	A	LD
Phoenix Guard	5	5	4	3	3	1	6	1	9
Keeper of the Flame	5	5	4	3	3	1	6	2	9

Unit Size:
5+

Weapons & Armour:
- Hand weapon
- Halberd
- Heavy armour

Special Rules:
- Valour of Ages
- Speed of Asuryan
- Cause *fear*
- Ward save (4+)

Options:

Command:
Upgrade one Phoenix Guard to a Keeper of the Flame **12pts**
  Keeper of the Flame may have magic items worth up to . .**25pts**
Upgrade one Phoenix Guard to a Musician **6pts**
Upgrade one Phoenix Guard to a Standard Bearer **12pts**
  Standard Bearer may have a magic standard worth up to . .**50pts**

White Lions of Chrace

Points/model: 15

	M	WS	BS	S	T	W	I	A	LD
White Lion	5	5	4	4	3	1	5	1	8
Guardian	5	5	4	4	3	1	5	2	8

Unit Size:
5+

Weapons & Armour:
- Hand weapon
- Woodsmans axe (Great weapon)
- Heavy armour
- Lion cloak

Special Rules:
- Valour of Ages
- Speed of Asuryan
- Woodsmen
- Lion cloak
- Stubborn

Options:

Command:
Upgrade one White Lion to a Guardian **12pts**
  Guardian may have magic items worth up to **25pts**
Upgrade one White Lion to a Musician **6pts**
Upgrade one White Lion to a Standard Bearer **12pts**
  Standard Bearer may have a magic standard worth up to . .**50pts**

SPECIAL

Silver Helms

	M	WS	BS	S	T	W	I	A	LD
Silver Helm	5	4	4	3	3	1	5	1	8
High Helm	5	4	4	3	3	1	5	2	8
Elven Steed	9	3	0	3	3	1	4	1	5

Unit Size:
5+

Weapons & Armour:
- Hand weapon
- Lance
- Heavy armour

Special Rules:
- Valour of Ages
- Speed of Asuryan

Mounts:
Barded Elven steed

Points/model: 21

Options:

Command:
Upgrade one Silver Helm to a High Helm 16pts
Upgrade one Silver Helm to a Musician 8pts
Upgrade one Silver Helm to a Standard Bearer 16pts

Additional equipment:
Shield . . . . 2pts per model

Dragon Princes of Caledor

	M	WS	BS	S	T	W	I	A	LD
Dragon Prince	5	5	4	3	3	1	6	2	9
Drakemaster	5	5	4	3	3	1	6	3	9
Elven steed	9	3	0	3	3	1	4	1	5

Unit Size:
5+

Weapons & Armour:
- Hand weapon
- Lance
- Dragon armour
- Shield

Special Rules:
- Valour of Ages
- Speed of Asuryan
- Dragon Armour

Mounts:
Barded Elven steed

Points/model: 30

Options:

Command:
Upgrade one Dragon Prince to a Drakemaster 20pts
   Drakemaster may have magic items worth up to 25pts
Upgrade one Dragon Prince to a Musician 10pts
Upgrade one Dragon Prince to a Standard Bearer 20pts
   Standard Bearer may have a magic standard worth up to . .50pts

Ellyrian Reavers

	M	WS	BS	S	T	W	I	A	LD
Ellyrian Reavers	5	4	4	3	3	1	5	1	8
Harbinger	5	4	5	3	3	1	5	1	8
Elven Steed	9	3	0	3	3	1	4	1	5

Unit Size:
5+

Weapons & Armour:
- Hand weapon
- Spear
- Light armour

Special Rules:
- Valour of Ages
- Speed of Asuryan
- Fast Cavalry

Mounts:
Elven steed

Points/model: 17

Options:

Command:
Upgrade one Ellyrian Reaver to a Harbinger 7pts
Upgrade one Ellyrian Reaver to a Musician 7pts
Upgrade one Ellyrian Reaver to a Standard Bearer 14pts

Additional equipment:
Bow . . . . .4pts per model
Swap spear for bow . . . . .2pts per model

SPECIAL

Shadow Warriors

	M	WS	BS	S	T	W	I	A	LD
Shadow Warrior	5	5	4	3	3	1	5	1	8
Shadow-walker	5	5	4	3	3	1	5	2	8

Unit Size:
5+

Weapons & Armour:
- Hand weapon
- Longbow
- Light armour

Special Rules:
- Valour of Ages
- Speed of Asuryan
- Nagarythe Hatred
- Scout
- Skirmish

Points/model: 16

Options:

Command:
Upgrade one Shadow Warrior to a Shadow-walker **12pts**

Tiranoc Chariot

	M	WS	BS	S	T	W	I	A	LD
Tiranoc Chariot	-	-	-	5	4	4	-	-	-
Crew	-	4	4	3	-	-	5	1	8
Elven Steed	9	3	-	3	-	-	4	1	-

Unit Size:
1

Weapons & Armour:
The crew are armed with a hand weapon, spear and bow.

Special Rules:
- Valour of Ages
- Speed of Asuryan
- Chariot

Points/model: 85

Crew:
2 High Elves.

Drawn by:
2 Elven steeds.

Armour Save:
5+

Lion Chariot of Chrace

	M	WS	BS	S	T	W	I	A	LD
Lion Chariot of Chrace	-	-	-	5	4	4	-	-	-
Crew	-	5	4	4	-	-	5	1	8
War Lions	8	5	-	5	-	-	4	2	-

Unit Size:
1

Weapons & Armour:
The crew are armed with hand weapons and Great weapons.

Special Rules:
- Valour of Ages
- Speed of Asuryan
- Chariot
- Cause *fear*

Points/model: 140

Crew:
2 White Lions of Chrace.

Drawn by:
2 War Lions.

Armour Save:
4+

---

*I*sha is the goddess of harvest and nature. She is depicted as an Elf woman full of life and beauty and is considered to be the mother of the whole Elven race. Isha is the patron goddess of the Everqueen, blessing her with wisdom and beauty, and it is through Isha that the Everqueen draws much of her power. Isha blesses the eternal glades and fields of Avelorn so that winter never blemishes the domain of the Everqueen.

It was Isha who taught the Elves how to care for the land and gain a plentiful harvest. The Symbol of Isha is the All Seeing Eye, shedding a single tear for her mortal children, the Elves. At the dawn of time Asuryan decided that while the Elves would be prodigiously long-lived, they would still grow weary of the world and die. Isha, who loved her children the Elves above all her creations, despaired and cried in anguish.

RARE

Repeater Bolt Thrower

Points/model: 100

	M	WS	BS	S	T	W	I	A	LD
Bolt Thrower	-	-	-	-	7	3	-	-	-
High Elf Crew	5	4	4	3	3	1	5	1	8

Crew:
2 High Elves

Unit Size:
1

Weapons & Armour:
The crew carry hand weapons and wear light armour.

Special Rules:
- Valour of Ages
- Speed of Asuryan
- Volley

Great Eagle

Points/model: 50

	M	WS	BS	S	T	W	I	A	LD
Great Eagle	2	5	0	4	4	3	4	2	8

Unit Size:
1

Weapons & Armour:
Talons
(a hand weapon).

Special Rules:
- Fly

VAUL'S FORGE

In this section, the common magic items are listed first (see the Warhammer rule book for a complete description). 'High Elf only' magic items are also listed and these can only be used by models from this book. Any magic items chosen must be selected within the points limitations set by the army list section. All the rules on magic items presented in the Warhammer rule book also apply to the 'High Elf only' magic items.

Common Magic Items

Sword of Striking   25 points
Weapon; +1 to hit.

Sword of Battle   20 points
Weapon; +1 Attack.

Sword of Might   15 points
Weapon; +1 Strength.

Biting Blade   10 points
Weapon; -1 to enemy armour saves.

Enchanted Shield   10 points
Armour; 5+ armour save.

Talisman of Protection   10 points
Talisman; 6+ Ward save.

Dispel Scroll   20 points
Arcane; automatically dispels an enemy spell. One use only.

Power Stone   20 points
Arcane; +2 dice to cast a spell. One use only.

Staff of Sorcery   40 points
Arcane; +1 to dispel.

War Banner   20 points
Banner; +1 Combat Resolution.

MAGIC WEAPONS

Blade of Leaping Gold   60 points
A more finely balanced sword than this was never made.

The blade confers +3 Attacks on the character wielding it.

Bow of the Seafarer   60 points
This longbow was made from a single piece of rare silverwood, and gifted to Ulanor of the Sea Guard by Finubar himself. It is a mighty weapon, and many say it can even sink ships!

Treat the Bow of the Seafarer as a normal longbow with the following exception. Resolve each hit like a single bolt from a Bolt Thrower (see the main rule book). Note that you may shoot after moving (but not marching) and stand & shoot with the Bow of the Seafarer.

Sword of Hoeth   60 points
Normally this fine blade lies wrapped in silk in the armoury of the White Tower, but in time of war it is given to a great hero to wield in the name of the Loremasters.

All hits wound automatically. Armour saves are modified by the Strength of the bearer.

Star Lance   40 points
An ancient weapon, famed throughout Caledor, the tip of the Star Lance is forged from the heart of a fallen star.

Mounted character only. Lance. This weapon follows the rules for lances, except that the bearer receives +3 strength, instead of +2 on the turn he charges. In addition, while mounted, when the bearer charges no armour saves can be made against this weapon.

Reaver bow   40 points
Some believe this wondrous bow is the same one that was forged for Prince Arathion of Ellyrion a thousand years ago.

Treat the Reaver Bow as a normal longbow with the following exceptions: the bearer may shoot three times at the same target in each of his Shooting phases and any hits are resolved at Strength 5.

The White Sword   40 points
A legendary blade forged for Aren, one of the first Sword Masters of Hoeth, it is as tall as an Elf, as light as a willow switch.

Model on foot only, requires two hands. The bearer adds +2 to his Strength when using the White Sword. In addition it confers the Killing Blow special rule.

Blade of Sea Gold   40 points
This gleaming blade is made from the finest sea gold, found in the dark depths of the sea and honed by crashing waves. It strikes with the unstoppable power of the sea itself.

No armour saves may be taken against wounds caused by the Blade of Sea Gold.

Foe Bane   25 points
This strange and twisted blade was taken from the body of a Chaos champion. Quite why he should have carried it is unknown, as is the name of the brave Elf that slew him.

All hits on a target with 2 or more Wounds on its starting profile will always wound on a 2+. Armour saves are modified by the Strength of the bearer as normal.

MAGIC ARMOUR

Armour of Protection   45 points

This simple suit of ithilmar armour is adorned by a single Sarathai rune on the breastplate. The World Dragon itself is said to protect the wearer.

Counts as light armour (armour save 6+) which can be combined with other equipment normally. It also provides a 4+ Ward save.

Golden Shield   35 points

A highly polished shield of blessed legend, inlaid with swirling patterns in many types of gold, its glory dazzles the foe and confuses their aim.

This shield confers a 6+ armour save which can be combined with other equipment normally. In addition, all successful attempts to hit the bearer in close combat must be re-rolled.

Armour of Stars   30 points

Mage-forged plate decorated with hundreds of glittering gems on a background of deepest blue lacquer, the Armour of Stars is a wonder to behold.

May only be worn by a model on foot. The Armour of Stars counts as light armour (armour save 6+) which can be combined with other equipment normally. If the wearer suffers an unsaved wound he is instantly teleported 3D6" in a random direction.

Note that this means that he can only suffer 1 unsaved wound in a round of close combat as he will be teleported away before the second can strike him. However, if he was struck by a Killing Blow or a weapon that does multiple wounds per hit (such as a cannon ball) then he would still suffer the instant death or multiplied wounds as normal before teleporting away.

If the model is teleported into another model or impassable terrain then simply carry on moving it along in the same direction until it is 1" beyond. If the model teleports off the table, then treat it as having pursued off.

Armour of Heroes   30 points

This finely wrought suit of armour is made in a most unusual style, not seen since before the Sundering. The wearer of this armour seems to shine with an inner light and the untold glories of the gods.

Counts as heavy armour (armour save 5+) which can be combined with other equipment normally. In order to allocate close combat attacks against the wearer, an opponent must first pass a Leadership test. Test each Close Combat phase. If the test is failed, the enemy may not attack.

Temakador's Gauntlets   30 points

Prince Temakador disliked harming fellow nobles in a duel, but he hated even more to be harmed himself.

These gauntlets grant a 6+ armour save which can be combined with other equipment normally. They also give the bearer a 5+ Ward save against attacks of Strength 4 or greater.

Shadow Armour   25 points

Forged by the bitter Shadow Warriors in their hidden camps, the shimmering Shadow Armour weighs almost nothing. It exists somewhere between the real world and that of magic, a fact which mages find quite alarming.

Counts as heavy armour (armour save 5+) which can be combined with other equipment normally. In addition, if the wearer is an independent character on foot then he has the Scout special rule. He may choose to deploy either at the same time as the other characters, or as a Scout (including setting up with a unit of Shadow Warriors).

Armour of Caledor   25 points

The ruling line of Caledor have passed this suit of armour from father to son for more than four thousand years.

Confers a 2+ armour save, that cannot be improved by any means. In addition, the Armour of Caledor follows the normal rules for Dragon armour on page 57.

Helm of Fortune   25 points

A helm of ithilmar and sea gold, bordered with tiny letters of intertwining runic script. These form a prayer to invoke Asuryan's protection upon the wearer.

This helm confers a 6+ armour save which can be combined with other equipment normally. The wearer may re-roll failed armour saves.

Dragonscale Shield   20 points

Although battered and scarred, this shield is a treasured heirloom of the days when Dragons roamed the skies.

This shield confers a 5+ armour save which can be combined with other equipment normally. Also gives the bearer a 6+ Ward save.

Mask of the Merlord   10 points

Discovered by Admiral Giladis, the gold surface of this strange war mask ripples with magical power.

Model on foot only. This mask confers a 6+ armour save which can be combined with other equipment normally. In addition, the wearer can move over marsh, rivers, lakes or any other water features without penalty, and will benefit from soft cover while in such terrain.

TALISMANS

Vambraces of Defence   55 points
These filigreed golden bracers are fabled to have been found on the shores of distant Lustria. The glyphs inscribed upon them writhe with untold power.

Gives the wearer a 4+ Ward save. In addition, the wearer may re-roll failed armour saves.

Golden Crown of Atrazar   40 points
This golden circlet, studded with rare and magical gems, radiates an aura that protects its wearer from harm.

One use only. Discount the first unsaved wound, even if it is a killing blow.

Loremaster's Cloak   40 points
Wrapped in this pale grey cloak, the wearer seems somehow insubstantial and almost illusory.

Gives the wearer and the unit he is with a 2+ Ward save against wounds caused by spells. It has no effect against shooting or close combat attacks.

Talisman of Saphery   35 points
The tiny size of this powerful artefact belies its true power.

The magical weapons of enemy models will have no special effects whilst they are in base contact with the bearer of the talisman. Treat the magic weapon as a normal one of its type, eg, a magic sword would count as a hand weapon, magic spear would count as a spear, etc.

Sacred Incense   30 points
Incense is often used in Elven rituals and this bundle of incense sticks has been blessed by the wardens of the Shrine of Asuryan. It will burn for days, wreathing the bearer with the scented smoke of the temples.

All shooting at the bearer or the unit he is with suffers a -1 to hit penalty.

Guardian Phoenix   25 points
A spark from the sacred flame at the temple of Asuryan is held in this ornate casket.

Gives the wearer a 5+ Ward save.

Amulet of Fire   20 points
Though the Amulet constantly flickers with pale flames, the wearer is never burned.

Gives the wearer Magic Resistance (1). In addition, the wearer cannot be harmed by Flaming Attacks.

MAGIC BANNERS

Battle Banner   80 points
This heavily woven banner is embroidered with detailed scenes of High Elf victories, and twinkles with the light of a thousand gemstones.

The unit may add +D6 to the combat resolution of any close combat in which it is involved.

Banner of the World Dragon   60 points
This magnificent standard is emblazoned with the glittering image of the World Dragon - a symbol of Ulthuan itself. It is made of the finest silks and cloth of gold, with a thousand emerald Dragon scales that sparkle in the firelight.

The unit is completely immune to all spell effects, whatever their source. This includes friendly spells, bound items, and spells with areas of effect that were cast on nearby units, etc. Spells which are cast on another unit, such as the Flaming Sword of Rhuin, will work as normal, as will all magic weapons used to attack them.

Banner of Sorcery   50 points
The Loremasters of Saphery presented this banner to King Finubar the Seafarer upon his coronation.

The banner adds +D3 Power dice to your pile in each of your own Magic phases.

Standard of Balance   45 points
Troubling shadows and flickering patches of light play across this banner as it flutters in the wind.

The unit carrying the Standard of Balance, and any enemy unit in base contact with it, is immune to psychology. In addition, they also lose hatred and frenzy abilities (in the same way as a unit that has already fought and lost a round of combat).

Banner of Arcane Protection   25 points
The fabric of this banner is steeped in magical energies, and interwoven with powerful protective charms.

The unit gets Magic Resistance (2).

Lion Standard   25 points
An aura of courage fills the hearts of those who serve under this banner, making them each as fierce as a lion!

The unit is immune to *fear* and *terror*.

Banner of Ellyrion   15 points
This small pennant of Korhandir, the father of all horses, imbues steeds with tireless energy to traverse the densest terrain.

The unit treats difficult ground as open ground for purposes of movement.

ARCANE ITEMS

Book of Hoeth   100 points
This well-worn tome has been studied by mages throughout the ages and has helped some of the greatest understand the inner workings of the realm of magic.

Any spell cast by the mage with this book will be cast with Irresistible Force on any successful casting roll which includes any double, except a Miscast.

The Vortex Shard   75 points
Hewn from the same rock that forms the waystones all over Ulthuan, the Vortex Shard has the power to becalm the Winds of Magic, if only for a moment.

One use only. The bearer may use the Vortex Shard at the start of any enemy Magic phase. The Magic phase ends immediately, all Remains in Play spells are dispelled and power dice stored in magic items are lost.

Annulian Crystal   40 points
Dug from beneath the Annuli Mountains, this crystal has been shaped by the magical vortex that swathes Ulthuan, so that it draws magical energy towards it.

During the enemy's Magic phase, the Crystal allows the High Elf player to remove one dice from the opponent's pile of Power dice and add it to his own Dispel dice pile.

Sigil of Asuryan   40 points
The sigil is tattooed on the hand of the mage using inks prepared in the sacred flame of Asuryan itself. After use it quickly fades away until it is renewed in the sacred flames once again.

Automatically dispels one enemy spell. In addition, roll a D6. On a 4+ the spell is destroyed and the casting Wizard cannot use it for the duration of the battle. One use only.

Starwood Staff   40 points
This gnarled and twisted staff looks out of place among the refined and delicately made possessions of the Elves. However, it is one of the most highly valued items a wizard can possess.

The Starwood staff gives +1 to all casting attempts made by the Wizard carrying it.

The Seerstaff of Saphery   30 points
Made from Starwood and crackling with powerful enchantments, the Seerstaff focuses the bearers' mind, allowing him to recall even the smallest details more clearly.

The bearer may choose his spells, instead of rolling for them at the start of the game.

The Trickster's Pendant   30 points
Few Elf Mages are devotees of Loec – the study of magic requires a less capricious patron. All those who seek favour of the Trickster wear a small pendant in his honour and such simple looking trinkets have unseen powers.

If an enemy Wizard suffers a Miscast he must roll twice on the Miscast table rather than once. The bearer of the Trickster's Pendant then chooses one of the two results. The chosen result is applied immediately. The other result is ignored and does not take effect.

The Gem of Sunfire   25 points
This ochre gemstone glows with the light and fury of the Sun even on the coldest of days. Only a Mage whose mastery of the most destructive sorceries can hope to tame its power.

One use only. At the start of any of his own Magic phases, the bearer may use the Gem of Sunfire. For the duration of that Magic phase, the bearer gains +2 to all his attempts to cast spells from the Lore of Fire for the rest of the Magic phase.

Ring of Corin   20 points
The origins of this ring are steeped in mystery, and no other artefacts of this powerful mage survive. However, few are the loremaster, wizards or warlocks that have not heard of it!

Bound spell (Power level 3). One use only. The Ring of Corin may cast its Bound spell in the Magic phase like an ordinary spell. The spell requires no Power dice to cast, all the power required is provided by the ring itself. The Ring of Corin contains the Vaul's Unmaking spell described in the High Magic spells on page 47.

Staff of Solidity   20 points
The Staff earths the malign energies of the Unseen Realm, dissipating any harm caused by unstable magic before it touches the mage.

This staff makes the Mage immune to the effects of his first Miscast. Note that a miscast spell still fails regardless of the actual dice score rolled.

Jewel of the Dusk   15 points
This fine ruby glows blood red with a sorcerous energy that even the least magically adept can clearly see.

The jewel gives the Mage +1 Power dice in each of his own Magic phases.

Silver Wand   10 points
This slender wand is covered with many lines of winding runes of the ancient script.

The wearer knows one more spell than is normal for his level.

ENCHANTED ITEMS

Null Stone   100 points
The Null Stone is a plain black rock, rough-hewn and undecorated. Those with the witch-sight see it as a dark void, an unsettling patch of nothingness in the world of magic.

No Wizard within 6" of the bearer may cast any spells. No other magic item or rune item within 6" of the bearer will work. Treat them as normal weapons, banners, etc, of the appropriate type. Note that this applies to all friendly wizards and magic items as well as enemy ones.

Healing Potion   50 points
A small vial of sky-blue liquid that sparkles in the light and holds the power to cheat death itself.

One use only. The character or any character in base contact may drink this at the start of any phase in either player's turn. It immediately restores all wounds lost by the character during the battle so far. Obviously, if the character is dead at the start of the phase then he can't drink the potion.

Radiant Gem of Hoeth   45 points
The gem is normally kept in a black velvet bag, carefully hiding its brilliance from prying eyes.

The wearer counts as a Level 1 High Elf Mage. This has no effect on characters who are already Wizards.

Folariath's Robe   45 points
This ancient vestment, that shimmers with the twinkling light of a thousand stars, was enchanted by the eccentric mage Folariath, who some say could walk between worlds.

Model on foot only. The wearer of this cloak can only be hit by magical attacks (for example, Magic weapons and attacks from Daemons or Ethereal creatures). In addition, the bearer may not strike blows in combat, or shoot with a ranged weapon.

Ring of Fury   40 points
The Elves are justly famed for their magical rings, and the black iron Ring of Fury is one of the most feared.

Bound spell (Power level 3). This ring may cast its Bound Spell once per Magic phase like an ordinary spell. The spell requires no Power dice to cast, all the power required is provided by the ring itself. The Ring of Fury contains the Fury of Khaine spell described in the High Magic spells on page 47.

Cloak of Beards   35 points
For millennia the High Elves have fought bitterly against the Dwarfs, collecting beards as a token payment for their black theft of the Phoenix Crown and weaving them into a cloak, that mocks and scorns the Dwarfs with its existence. Such is the enmity focussed in this item that Dwarf runes, the pride of their race, are drained of their power if they come too close.

Dwarfs both Hate and Fear the wearer of the Cloak. In addition, for the duration of each Close Combat phase, each model in base contact with the wearer loses all the runes from one of their runic items (determined randomly). Treat the item as a normal one of its kind.

Pendant of Vengeance   35 points
Enraged by the cowardly Dwarf Runesmiths whose Anvils of Doom wrought such ruination upon the High Elves in the War of the Beard, Aeoliss Loremaster of Hoeth created his masterpiece – the Pendant of Vengeance.

All successful strikings on the Anvil of Doom must be re-rolled. In addition, subtract -1 from any results on the Failed Rune table.

Dragonhorn   25 points
Enchanted by the dying flames of an ancient fire drake, the Dragonhorn hardens wavering hearts and strengthens resolve.

One use only. Once per battle, at the start of any of his own turns, the bearer may sound the horn. All friendly High Elf models may re-roll any failed Rally and Psychology tests until the start of their next turn.

The Skeinsliver   25 points
A fragment from the fabled Crown of Stars, this glittering metal splinter can give the bearer some small knowledge of the future, and thus the ability to shape destiny.

The Skeinsliver allows the controlling player to add +1 to the roll to determine which player takes the first turn.

The Amulet of Light   15 points
A small brooch first worn by Kalin Silverhair during the wars against the Daemons.

All attacks made by the bearer (and the unit he is with) in close combat count as Magical.

The Gem of Courage   10 points
Enchanted by Celaer in the reign of Bel-Korhadris, these small gems are frequently awarded by the Phoenix King for acts of incredible bravery.

One use only. The bearer (and the unit he is with) may take any one Leadership based test on 3D6, choosing the lowest two.

Talisman of Loec   10 points
Loec the Trickster is seldom worshipped on the battlefield by the High Elves, for his help always comes at a price.

One use only. This item is used at the start of any Close Combat phase. The bearer may re-roll all rolls to hit and wound until the end of the phase. Any model wounded by his attacks this phase must re-roll any successful saves of any kind. At the end of the phase the bearer suffers one wound with no saves of any kind allowed.

REFERENCE

LORDS	M	WS	BS	S	T	W	I	A	Ld	Special Rules	Page
Alith Anar	5	7	7	4	3	3	9	4	10	Valour of Ages, Speed of Asuryan, Nagarythe Hatred, Scout	90
Archmage	5	4	4	3	3	3	5	1	9	Valour of Ages, Speed of Asuryan	91
Eltharion	5	8	6	4	3	3	8	4	10	Valour of Ages, Speed of Asuryan, Hates Goblins, Blood Oath	90
Stormwing	6	6	0	5	5	5	7	4	8		
Prince	5	7	6	4	3	3	8	4	10	Valour of Ages, Speed of Asuryan	91
Teclis	5	3	3	2	2	3	5	1	10	Valour of Ages, Speed of Asuryan, High Loremaster	90
Tyrion	5	9	7	4	3	4	10	4	10	Valour of Ages, Speed of Asuryan, Defender of Ulthuan	90
Malhandir	10	4	0	4	3	1	5	2	7		

HEROES	M	WS	BS	S	T	W	I	A	Ld	Special Rules	Page
Caradryan	5	6	6	4	3	2	7	3	9	Valour of Ages, Speed of Asuryan, Causes Fear, Magic Resistance, Mark of Asuryan, 4+ Ward Save	92
Dragon Mage	5	4	4	3	3	2	6	2	8	Valour of Ages, Speed of Asuryan, Reckless, Warrior Mage	93
Korhil	5	6	6	4	3	2	7	3	9	Valour of Ages, Speed of Asuryan, Woodsmen, Stubborn	92
Mage	5	4	4	3	3	2	5	1	8	Valour of Ages, Speed of Asuryan	93
Noble	5	6	6	4	3	2	7	3	9	Valour of Ages, Speed of Asuryan	92

CORE	M	WS	BS	S	T	W	I	A	Ld	Special Rules	Page
Archer	5	4	4	3	3	1	5	1	8	Valour of Ages, Speed of Asuryan	94
Hawkeye	5	4	5	3	3	1	5	1	8		
Sea Guard	5	4	4	3	3	1	5	1	8	Valour of Ages, Speed of Asuryan, Martial Prowess	94
Sea Master	5	4	4	3	3	1	5	2	8		
Spearman	5	4	4	3	3	1	5	1	8	Valour of Ages, Speed of Asuryan, Martial Prowess	94
Sentinel	5	4	4	3	3	1	5	2	8		

SPECIAL	M	WS	BS	S	T	W	I	A	Ld	Special Rules	Page
Dragon Prince	5	5	4	3	3	1	6	2	9	Valour of Ages, Speed of Asuryan, Dragon Armour	96
Drakemaster	5	5	4	3	3	1	6	3	9		
Ellyrian Reavers	5	4	4	3	3	1	5	1	8	Valour of Ages, Speed of Asuryan, Fast Cavalry	96
Harbinger	5	4	5	3	3	1	5	1	8		96
Lion Chariot	-	-	-	5	4	4	-	-	-	Valour of Ages, Speed of Asuryan, Chariot, Cause Fear	97
Crew	-	5	4	4	-	-	5	1	8		
War Lions	8	5	-	5	-	-	4	2	-		97
Phoenix Guard	5	5	4	3	3	1	6	1	9	Valour of Ages, Speed of Asuryan, Cause Fear, Ward Save (4+)	95
Keeper o/t Flame	5	5	4	3	3	1	6	2	9		
Shadow Warrior	5	5	4	3	3	1	5	1	8	Valour of Ages, Speed of Asuryan, Nagarythe Hatred, Scout, Skirmish	97
Shadow-Walker	5	5	4	3	3	1	5	2	8		
Sword Master	5	6	4	3	3	1	5	2	8	Valour of Ages, Speed of Asuryan	95
Bladelord	5	6	4	3	3	1	5	3	8		
Tiranoc Chariot	-	-	-	5	4	4	-	-	-	Valour of Ages, Speed of Asuryan, Chariot	97
Crew	-	4	4	3	-	-	5	1	8		
Elven steed	9	3	-	3	-	-	4	1	-		
Silver Helm	5	4	4	3	3	1	5	1	8	Valour of Ages, Speed of Asuryan	96
High Helm	5	4	4	3	3	1	5	2	8		
White Lion	5	5	4	4	3	1	5	1	8	Valour of Ages, Speed of Asuryan, Woodsmen, Lion Cloak, Stubborn	95
Guardian	5	5	4	4	3	1	5	2	8		

RARE	M	WS	BS	S	T	W	I	A	Ld	Special Rules	Page
Bolt Thrower	-	-	-	-	7	3	-	-	-	Valour of Ages, Speed of Asuryan, Volley	98
Crew	5	4	4	3	3	1	5	1	8		
Great Eagle	2	5	0	4	4	3	4	2	8	Fly	93, 98

MOUNT	M	WS	BS	S	T	W	I	A	Ld	Special Rules	Page
Elven steed	9	3	0	3	3	1	4	1	5		93, 96, 97
Griffon	6	5	0	5	5	4	5	4	7	Fly, Large Target, Terror	93
Moon Dragon	6	6	0	6	6	6	3	5	8	Fly, Large Target, Terror, Scaly Skin, Dragon Fire	93
Star Dragon	6	7	0	7	6	7	2	6	9	Fly, Large Target, Terror, Scaly Skin, Dragon Fire	93
Sun Dragon	6	5	0	5	6	5	4	4	7	Fly, Large Target, Terror, Scaly Skin, Dragon Fire	93